Preliminary Edition Notice

You have been selected to receive a copy of this book in the form of a preliminary edition. This edition is used in a classroom setting to test the overall value of a book's content and ....s in a practical course prior to its formal publication on the national market.

As you use this text in your course, please share any and all feedback regarding the volume with your professor. Your comments on this text will allow the author to further develop the content of the book, so we can ensure it will be a useful and informative classroom tool for students in universities across the nation and around the globe. If you find the material is challenging to understand, or could be expanded to improve the usefulness of the text, it is important for us to know. If you have any suggestions for improving the material contained in the book or the way it is presented, we encourage you to share your thoughts.

Please note, preliminary editions are similar to review copies, which publishers distribute to select readers prior to publication in order to test a book's audience and elicit early feedback; therefore, you may find inconsistencies in formatting or design, or small textual errors within this volume. Design elements and the written text will likely undergo changes before this book goes to print and is distributed on the national market.

This text is not available in wide release on the market, as it is actively being prepared for formal publication. Accordingly, the book is offered to you at a discounted price to reflect its preliminary status.

If you would like to provide notes directly to the publisher, you may contact us by e-mailing studentreviews@cognella.com. Please include the book's title, author, and 7-digit SKU reference number (found below the barcode on the back cover of the book) in the body of your message.

The Novel Researcher

What You Need to Know Before Doing Research

Revised Preliminary Edition

Adelina Holguin

University of Texas – El Paso

Bassim Hamadeh, CEO and Publisher
John Remington, Senior Field Acquisitions Editor
Michelle Piehl, Project Editor
Abbey Hastings, Associate Production Editor
Miguel Macias, Senior Graphic Designer
Stephanie Kohl, Licensing Associate
Emily Bolender, Production Assistant
Natalie Piccotti, Senior Marketing Manager
Kassie Graves, Vice President of Editorial
Jamie Giganti, Director of Academic Publishing

Table of Contents

Chapter 1: The Novel Researcher

*"Treat people as if they were what they ought to be and you help them to become
what they are capable of being."*

–Johann Wolfgang von Goethe

Who is the Novel Researcher?

The novel researcher (or novice; which will be used interchangeably throughout the book) as defined within the context of this book refers to an individual that has no prior training or experience in conducting research. The novel researcher most often is thought of as a student—an undergraduate or starting graduate student—either volunteering or working on research projects, or as students in secondary school participating in research programs. Also, an individual may consider him- or herself a novice if he or she is participating in research not within an academic setting and with no formal training or guidance provided. An individual that engages in research without the mentorship from a trained researcher or formal class instruction may not, on his or her own, develop the skills and knowledge that are necessary to perform research.

Then what is research? Research is a methodolgy that applies problem-solving skills and reasoning to answer questions. Research can be exhilirating and highly engaging, but without the proper skill sets or adequate preparation, the research experience can be disheartening and frustrating. Without research training the practice of conducting research may result in misleading information. Consequently, the significance of the phenomenon may not be interpreted accurately.

When does the novice researcher become an expert researcher then? Although years of experience matter when distinguishing the novice from the expert, the difference between the novice and expert researcher rests on the acquired knowledge gained over those years. However, to acquire that knowledge it can take years for the expertise to develop. To develop an expertise requires dedication to a field and extensive reading. The existing literature must be understood to identify the gaps in the reasoning. Once a well-developed understanding of the literature is formed, new ideas can be proposed to advance research in a particular field. The novice that expresses a fascination for research and reads the literature that forms his or her own ideas can approach expertise level; however, becoming knowledgeable in research requires time to develop expertise, and a steadfast approach should be taken. So does a novice researcher only need to be well-versed in the literature to become an expert? The answer is no; the novice researcher must know how to interpret data and discern the direction the research should take. The novice must also know the integral role that ethics play in research. Without an understanding of how ethics affect research, just having a well-developed knowledge–literature base is a moot point because ethics are interwoven in the fabric of research. Also, the expert researcher has an extended network of colleagues in the field to tap into to discuss current issues that may be affecting a particular research field.

Preconceived Perceptions

One notable characteristic of the novice is the perception of what entails research. For example, a novice may have a misconception of the level of commitment required, both physically and mentally to answer research questions. To engage in a research career requires an internal motivational drive that is filled with curiosity and ardor. The novice may not be well-aware that researchers very rarely derive answers from one trial experiment but that small strides add up to great breakthroughs. Research for the most part progresses slowly; therefore, a level of resiliency and patience is required to press on to pursue research questions. Because novices are by the most part students—undergraduates or graduate students—there is a misconception that an entire experiment can be completed from start to finish over a semester or summer session. This misconception can lead to disappointment if the student does not have the adequate time to spend working on the project to see an experiment come to fruition. Students starting in a research setting can become very excited to be in a laboratory and to handle equipment and use supplies. The novice may have a notion that the technical part of experimenting is the research part. The idea that performing technical activities is all there is to research is misguided. The novice soon learns that what comes before and after the technical part is research.

Self-Identifying as a Researcher

In any profession, individuals associate with their job, and the specific duties that are carried out help form a self-identity with that occupation. Occupations such as medical doctors, police officers, or military officials impact the dedication and quality of the occupational performance. The same applies to an individual attracted to the field of research. A young individual new to research may not self-identify as a researcher because he or she may believe that a degree must first be obtained. A degree must be earned to gain employment in research, but self-identifying as a researcher occurs when self-awareness happens in his or her own ability and capacity to do research is gained. The novice becomes more comfortable with the notion that in research, making mistakes is part of the research process, and that something is always learned from experiments that do not work out. Furthermore, a researcher is not defined by how successful and how quickly experiments happen, but by the methodical research approach and the diligence by which new questions are formed to keep carving out a path to new discoveries. An individual that performs the technical research duties may not necessarily see him- or herself as a researcher. However, an individual that develops the ideas, formulates the questions, and interprets the findings will more readily develop a self-identity as a researcher. The earlier a self-identification as a researcher forms, the earlier a self-fulfilling research career can start to form.

Benefits of Reading this Book

What will a research foundations book do for the novice researcher? It lays the foundation for the novice researcher to define science (Chapter 2); to become aware of the various applications of research (Chapter 2); to develop research questions, frame hypotheses, and design experiments (Chapter 3); to recognize the application of statistics in research (Chapter 4); to recognize the various types of scientific literature (Chapter 5); to recognize ethical behavior in a research setting (Chapter 6); to record or document research (Chapter 7); and to design scientific presentations that effectively communicate research findings (Chapter 8). The last chapter is dedicated to group work and how to use it to achieve academic success (Chapter 9).

As the novice develops a literary research background, he or she can take a path of well thought-out ideas that will steer him or her through discovering the infinite that remains to be known.

End-of-Chapter Exercises: Applying Concepts

1. Explain who the novel researcher is.
   2. List three misconceptions that a novel researcher may have about research.
   3. Explain why it is important to form a self-identity as a researcher.

Chapter 2: Defining Science

"Equipped with his five senses, man explores the universe around him and calls the adventure Science."

–Edwin Powell Hubble

Learning Objectives:

1. Define what science is.
2. Explain scientific criteria.
3. Explain the scientific method.

Does scientific inquiry have to meet all the criteria to be accepted as scientific?

Search for Truth

Science is the search for truth that explains natural phenomena and encompasses everything between what is infinitesimally small and what is as vast as the universe. This definition is a straightforward explanation of science; however, the question debated throughout history is: What qualifies as scientific? What approaches or explanations put forth to explain an unknown phenomenon are accepted as scientific? In everyday life, people make judgments or have opinions of their surroundings based on observations made of their surroundings or environment. Where does the line lie that distinguishes an opinion from something scientific? To answer the previous question, a historical comparison is provided of two distinct approaches about the same phenomenon.

Opinion to Scientific

A historical anecdote that reflects on the observations by Aristotle and centuries later by Galileo Galilei on falling objects provides a perspective of how individuals are persuaded to believe natural phenomenon; Aristotle claimed that objects that are heavier reached the ground faster than lighter ones. Aristotle's observation was an opinion because his claim was not substantiated by any means other than seeing objects fall and deducing that heavier objects reached the ground faster than lighter objects. No further investigation of the phenomenon of falling objects ensued following Aristotle's observations. The conclusion reached by Aristotle was readily believed by the masses because the experience of watching a feather falling compared with a stone falling made a strong case for his claims. Aristotle's observations went unchecked for centuries until Galileo Galilei challenged them. Galileo's methodological approach demonstrated that Aristotle's observations had neglected key variables such as the orientation of the object and the air resistance it met as it traveled downward. The variables that Galileo succeeded in demonstrating were the determinants of how fast an object traveled through the air. After centuries had passed since Aristotle's unchallenged theory, Galileo's theory convinced others because of his carefully crafted experiments that permitted witness of his reasoning of falling objects.

In science, it is not always possible to directly witness a line of reasoning put forth by theorists. Galileo was faced with the challenge of convincing others of a phenomenon that was not possible for most people to accept because his claim was not readily observable and was strongly opposed by one of the dominating influences of that time—religion. Galileo's efforts to convince the church that a geocentric view was not the truth were met with unwavering resistance. In his quest for truth, Galileo pursued Nicholas Copernicus's theories that the earth revolved around the sun and not the other way around. If the same argument were made today, Galileo would not experience such opposition because of the technological advances that allow earthlings to observe their planet from space. In the present time, it seems impossible to believe that there was a time that the belief that the world revolved around the sun (Copernican theory), and not the other way around (Geocentric) was the point of grave contention that lead to prohibiting such claims from reaching the masses. Galileo's challenge to expose the truth was to change the masses' view that contradicted their daily experience, that the sun was the phenomenon that moved and not the earth. It would be an understatement to say that Copernicus and then Galileo, and other like scientists, took on the challenge to show that the "truth" was what people were unable to observe—that the earth was the body that was moving. Galileo used mathematical models, and through observations of another planet's phases (technology not available during Copernicus's time), he provided significant evidence to refute the geocentric view. Galileo's stance on the geocentric view provoked an intense pushback prohibiting his works from public access. His evidence was eventually shared with the public but not for many years later.

Through his experiments, Galileo was able to successfully repudiate previously proposed theories, e.g., heavier objects fall faster, and the sun revolved around the earth, to demonstrate that what seemed obvious and readily believable was not necessarily the truth. Galileo succeeded because he added an element of "disproving" the theories that he challenged through his experiments to seek truths of natural phenomenon. Galileo would be satisfied to know how his theories can now be readily observed and reproduced through methodologies that he developed, i.e., experimentation.

What is scientific? Most would argue that the search for truths or scientific inquiry must be able to "disprove" current beliefs, observations must be measurable, and the methodologies must be reproducible.

Principle of Falsifiability

Was Aristotle's observation an opinion and Galileo's observation scientific? For a claim about how a phenomenon happens in nature to be considered scientific it requires refutation. An unrefuted phenomenon in some form or another is not scientific, according to the principle of falsifiability. The principle of falsifiability argues that a hypothesis must be "disproved" when in search of the truth of an unexplained phenomenon. Otherwise, it cannot be known with any certainty that the explanation of the phenomenon is a truth if that truth cannot refute it. If it is a truth, then the phenomenon should withstand examination over time.

Empirical Evidence and Reproducibility

In line with the principle of falsifiability, a scientific inquiry must include empirical evidence and reproducibility. These criteria support claims of an unknown phenomenon to be true. *Empirical evidence* is an observation that can be measured. For example, if a scientist claims that global warming is happening, trends in increasing temperatures can be observed over time to show that the earth is warming. The rising temperatures can be easily observed by measuring the temperature. Yet, global warming remains a point of contention, argued that the increasing temperatures are a result of normal global changes. Scientists argue that the rate of increasing temperatures is a result of pollutants such as emissions that are deteriorating the ozone layer of the atmosphere. Although evidence continues to mount toward global warming as a consequence of pollutants, this issue continues to be challenged because the argument is made that natural global changes have not been definitively ruled out as the cause for increasing temperatures or that the evidence presented by environmentalists does not comprehensively point to pollutants as the only cause of global warming. In instances where phenomena were not readily observed, as was the case of the Copernican theory, scientists developed mathematical models and studied other planets' positions using telescopes; intuitive reasoning provided the evidence to uncover truths that were eventually accepted, as in the case of global warming.

Today, technology aims to see phenomena that are beyond the grasp of the human senses. Earth can be seen from space, and marine life can be discovered from the depths of the ocean. Technology, an extension of human senses, helps us to learn about the most infinitesimal matter that exists, i.e., atoms. Atoms—the building blocks of matter—are of microscopic dimensions and require highly specialized microscopes to extrapolate information of structure and dimensions. All living and nonliving things are composed of atoms. Everything that humans have created stems from the interactions between atoms that occur naturally or are synthesized. A sense of amazement is felt when standing in front of a tall building with the knowledge that those structures are formed from an infinitesimal number of atoms.

Reliability and Validity

How can scientists build structures if they cannot directly see atoms? Hallmarks of large cities are tall buildings. Great scientific minds have applied their ingenuity to create these buildings by manipulating matter to form materials that support the structure's foundation, such as iron and concrete. Rigorous testing of the materials' stability is conducted. The repeated process of testing, i.e., *reproducibility,* is fundamental to defining science. How would reproducibility apply to mathematical equations? Scientists rely on mathematical equations in the absence of direct observation and through repeated testing, which shows consistency in the results that can then be claimed as laws. The laws of matter are then applied to form hypotheses. For example, chemical equations are relied upon to test how atoms interact with each other. The combinations of atom interactions based on chemical equations become the foundation of the construction of structures. The durability of these structures is dependent on the laws of matter. Because of established laws, the structures that have stood tall for centuries withstanding the fiercest of temperatures, winds, and waters can be said to demonstrate *reliability* (consistency of what is claimed to test or detect), or science at its best. Reliability has limitations; however, the probability that a test will fail is always a possibility.

Technology has become the personal assistant to scientific query because there is no area of science or discipline that does not in some form or another use or apply technology. In laboratories, technology has become indispensable for equipment that can measure DNA, e.g., the polymerase chain reaction (PCR) machine. Outside the laboratory, sonar equipment is used to study sea life in the field of acoustic oceanography. Although technology can be said to be an extension of our five senses, all technology has limitations, and those that depend on technology must work within those limitations. Equipment is limited in its level of detection, and that level of detection is what scientists depend on for the precision of their measurements they claim to test or detect. The accuracy of the test provides validity of the measurements. Because DNA is invisible to the naked eye, and quantifiable amounts of DNA are necessary to detect, the PCR machine can duplicate DNA in quantifiable amounts. The end product provides an estimated amount of how much DNA was in the original sample. A PCR machine requires a certain amount of DNA for the machine to detect the DNA and amplify it within a certain precision or validity. Likewise, sonar equipment, a tool to detect marine life, has its limitations because of a few parameters that include the settings of the equipment, its degree of frequencies, and its position and orientation of the organisms in the water (Fornshell & Tesei, 2013). Scientists are dependent upon the validity and reliability of the equipment used to obtain measurements that help explain a phenomenon. Technology is continuously improved upon to increase the reliability and validity of measurements because without it, the pace of science would not keep up with events that impact Earth and the universe.

Scientific Method

The scientific method follows a logical order to test *hypotheses*. The first step is to identify a problem. There is a wealth of scientific literature that guides researchers through information about phenomena that is not yet well-understood. With a thorough sleuthing of the existing literature, gaps that exist in the literature can be identified. Those gaps in the literature that are unexplained phenomenon lead to forming novel hypotheses. To test hypotheses, scientists develop methods and procedures that form the *experimental design*. In conducting the experiment, data is derived or *results* that then can be interpreted to form *conclusions* or analyses of data. The conclusions should make a transition to what is the next logical step or next question.

Novel Findings through Experimentation

While experiments are underway, very unexpected outcomes may happen that uncover new phenomena and can steer the course of an entire research discipline. One classic example was challenging the widely-accepted molecular process involving the decoding of genetic information to protein synthesis. The belief was that the sequence in decoding genetic information could only happen from DNA to RNA then to protein synthesis, a process known as the central dogma of molecular biology. The discovery of retroviruses that use a host's cellular machinery to transcribe the viral RNA to host DNA was the first revelation that challenged the central dogma. Additional molecular and protein mechanisms are now reported to circumvent the central dogma of molecular biology.

A classic case that demonstrates how a phenomenon was discovered while performing experiments involving physiological processes led to the unraveling of psychological states in associated learning. These psychological discoveries are credited to the ingenious observations by Ivan Petrovich Pavlov, a physiologist who also became well-known for his experiments that had psychological relevance. Pavlov was interested in the digestion of food and performed his studies using dogs. Pavlov measured the amount of saliva the dogs produced while they were digesting food after being fed. However, after a few feedings the dogs started to salivate before being fed. This physiological response annoyed Pavlov because it intervened with his experimentation. Nonetheless, the unexplained observation sparked his curiosity to investigate the novel phenomenon. Through rigorous experiments, he discovered that the dogs appeared to salivate when presented with objects immediately before being offered food, but those items were inanimate and not associated in any form to food, e.g., a bell. He repeated his observations using other objects and came to the conclusion that the dogs were exhibiting a conditioned reflex in which they were pairing the object to the food. When presented with an object followed by food, the dog would salivate. The pairing of the object with food became so strongly associated that the dog would salivate in the absence of food. The phenomenon became known as *Pavlovian conditioning* or *classical conditioning*. The significance of Pavlov's discovery was enlightening because he had illustrated a mechanism of learning necessary for survival. The ability of organisms to associate environmental cues (bell) to those cues that benefit survival (food) can increase the probabilities of organisms' survival. For example, the rancid smell of milk will dissuade someone from drinking it, because the smell of rancid milk is associated with spoiled milk that if consumed will inevitably result in gastrointestinal discomfort. Similarly, conditioned learning in the wild is highly beneficial because animals learn defensive behaviors to avoid being eaten. (Pavlov's experiments were with dogs; nowadays it is unethical to perform investigations using dogs.)

Defining Research

It is not unusual to use science and research interchangeably. Research implies the systematic approach to discover truths of unexplained natural phenomenon, or it applies the *scientific method.* Research involves scientific inquiry, the practical application in experimentation, and interpreting findings. The act of performing research is to gain knowledge and use that knowledge to improve, develop, and promote quality of life. Research branches into various types of practices: *basic research*, *applied research*, *clinical research*, *translational research*, and *biomedical research*. Therefore, a multidisciplinary approach can answer scientific inquiries better through a multifaceted approach than one discipline on its own.

Types of Research

Basic research primarily happens in the laboratory setting. This type of research may follow hypothesis-driven questions. In an example such as research of antibiotic-resistant bacteria, basic research would involve deciphering the bacterial biological and chemical processes used by the bacteria to evade antibiotic effectiveness from which the bacteria develop antibiotic-resistant properties to antibiotics. *Applied research* can follow the same methodology as basic research; however, it tests theories in the practical sense. *Field* and *clinical* research can be classified as applied research. For example, a highly active *field research* is in field crops' pesticide control and water contamination projects. *Clinical research* is performed with humans that provide medical information from large groups of individuals such as testing a new drug to treat an infection. *Translation research* is also in line with clinical research with the purpose of transferring the findings derived in the laboratory to clinical or field research settings. For example, drug testing starts in the laboratory setting and reaches the clinical trials stage. *Biomedical research* focuses on developing technologies and methodologies that focus on health issues. Biomedical research can involve both models and/or human research. Models, as the word suggest, are used in lieu of human beings to learn about the human condition in health or sickness. Models can be animals, insects, and even technology. (For more on models see Chapter 3: Experimental Design.)

The idea of the "sole scientists" working alone in the laboratory is not the norm in today's fast-paced technological atmosphere with the complex problems facing society in health, technology, defense, and the environment. *Multidisciplinary research* brings together the expertise of different disciplines (biology, chemistry, physics, psychology, and engineering to mention a few) to combine efforts that will address problems from various perspectives. Today's breaking ground innovations from multidisciplinary research efforts are discovering the intricate workings of the brain or *neuronal activity* through collaborations from various disciplines that include physics, engineering, neuroscience, biology, and chemistry (Gibney, 2015).

Who Does Research?

Research is most often associated with academic institutions, such as two- or four-year secondary education institutions; however, primary schools also practice research with the objective to prepare students for post-secondary education. Research is also conducted by governmental agencies (e.g., military) and the private sector (e.g., pharmaceutical companies).

Academic Research

In academia, a hierarchical structure exists with different levels of academics that perform research including full professors, associate professors, and assistant professors. The professors are primarily the principle investigators (PI) in their areas of expertise. They are funded through governmental and private sector grants and can also receive donations from the private sector. Normally the second tier comprises the postdoctoral (after the doctoral training), which can also have different titles such as research postdoctoral, research associate professors, or senior research associates. The latter two are individuals who may have more than three years of postdoctoral experience and have developed expertise in a research area; however, they work under the auspices of a professor who may provide funding and resources to support the research. The next level is the graduate student who is in the process of completing a master's or Ph.D. degree (or predoctoral). Undergraduates, which may include freshmen to seniors, are also part of the academic research infrastructure. Although undergraduates are new to the academic arena, they are an integral part of research, and their fresh views can offer new perspectives on research projects. Graduates' and undergraduates' research projects are mostly supervised and guided under the PI and the postdoctoral.

Government (Military) Research

The military has an array of research scopes from defense technologies to behavioral studies. The United States Army Research Laboratory covers all areas of research that help soldiers perform their jobs with advanced defense technology such as extramural basic research. Additionally, the military invests in its soldiers' well being by incorporating behavioral sciences focused on mental health.

Private Sector Research

Research that happens in the private sector encompasses health care (e.g., pharmaceutical companies and healthcare facilities), technology, and marketing. With today's flexible communication channels, the different lines of research (academia, government, and the private sector) intersect in research efforts. The pharmaceutical industry's innovations take place continuously to find therapeutics that can be noninvasive, produce minimal or no side effects, and can be accessible to those who need treatment. Innovations in drug delivery using nanotechnologies are currently a major research endeavor for pharmaceuticals and the health industry. The possibility that a drug can be directly delivered to the intended site such as a tumor without producing side effects makes using nanotechnology and transforming drug delivery for diseases a potential for better prognosis. The integration of technology in all aspects of life cannot be overstated. Technological advances in health care such as prosthetics or pacemakers bring hope to individuals that otherwise may be limited in their daily living functions. The marketing industries use technology to reach the masses to gather information and make predictions about consumer preferences. Surveys are now commonplace for multimedia in the quest to gather information about a specific product or service. Unlike other research fields, market research analysis only requires a bachelor's degree, collects data using surveys, interviews, or focus groups, and then interprets the data and recommends strategies to help a company best serve its consumers and edge out a competitor.

The Research Cycle

The research cycle follows the logic of the scientific method. The novice can start the research cycle by sleuthing through the available knowledge, i.e., *scientific literature*. It is good practice, especially for the novice, to begin with reading the scientific literature to be informed about a particular subject and to identify what areas of that subject remain unanswered. The novice may have an idea of a broader topic to *investigate*, for example, current intense research efforts are focused on the effects of curcumin (the ingredient of turmeric) on tumor growth. Searching a specific area of research, such as a search for curcumin effects on tumor growth, may be overwhelming for the novice and result in an extensive literature list; hence, the novice should start with narrowing the topic to help focus the research and increase the specificity of the topic. A thorough literature search is necessary to achieve a well-informed knowledge level on a topic or research area. With a knowledge base that has depth and breadth, the unknowns or gaps in the literature can be identified and explained. Also, sleuthing through the literature, the novice can decipher the methodologies or experimentation that have been used. At that point, the novice can obtain information that will guide him or her to the next step in the research cycle. The next step involves deciphering from the following: 1) Is the information already known?, 2) Can an established methodology be used, or is there a need to develop a new methodology?, and/or 3) Will it require more than one discipline to address the problem? Having these questions answered while reading the literature will help formulate *hypotheses*. Once a hypothesis statement is formulated, an experiment design (experimental design) that will test the hypothesis can be developed (see Chapter 3: Experimental Design). Data is then generated or collected, i.e., *data collection*. The interpretation of the data derives results. These results now form new information and can be written in the form of a *manuscript* that can be submitted for publication through a process known as *peer review*. The peer review starts with the editor of the scientific journal doing one of three things: 1) make an academic determination that the manuscript does not meet most of the criteria and reject the submission, 2) qualify the manuscript to meet the criteria, followed by a review by the editor, or 3) submit the manuscript for review by other experts in the field. In the event the third option happens, that editor will submit the manuscript to two or three experts for review. The experts make one of three decisions based on their expert input: 1) decline the manuscript, 2) accept the manuscript with revisions or request further experimentation, or 3) accept the manuscript as submitted (though this is rare). Once the manuscript goes through the peer review process and is accepted for publication, the new information in the article now becomes part of the existing scientific literature.

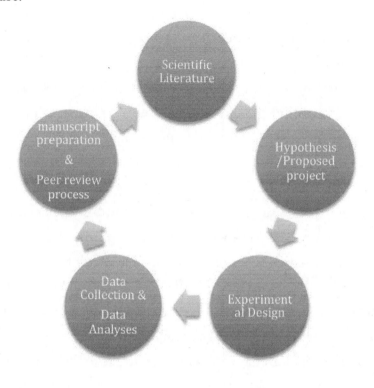

Figure 2.1

Dimensions of Science

Within the scientific community, the consensus of what constitutes as scientific is, in fact, a short list of criteria: 1) it should have a component of falsifiability, 2) it should be reproducible, and 3) its observations should be measured or empirical. Collectively, these criteria provide reliability and validity to ascertain a phenomenon truth, and that truth can be explained. It seems simple enough; however, not all scientific quests meet all the criteria, yet are considered scientific. Case studies are not necessarily reproducible but are considered research because the information describes an unknown condition that forms a piece of a puzzle that with enough case studies, new criteria can be developed, for instance, the symptomatology of a particular medical condition. The *Diagnostic and Statistical Manual of Mental Disorders (DSM)* classifies symptomatology of mental disorders, such as the mental decline observed in HIV case studies. The information reported from the case studies accumulated over time helps form a history of symptoms that are now categorized and classified. The classification of HIV-associated mental disorders helped distinguish symptoms that presented in children or adults as well as helped determine the disease's neurological progression.

Research may also be limited by the inability to measure the observations directly but relies on other means that provide empirical evidence. A chemist depends on technology to decipher chemical structures and orientations and relies on these indirect observations to then develop mathematical models to form chemical reactions. The last example is limited in empirical evidence and is still regarded as research. A psychologist interested in therapeutic treatments for individuals that suffer from posttraumatic stress, or is interested in after-school programs for at-risk adolescents, can be limited in experiment reproducibility. The data collected from the last examples rely mostly on self-reports; relying on the participants' own perceptions of their reported level of improvement (or not) leaves ample room for subjectivity in the data as a result of the nature of self-reports. However, the practice is recognized as research because it forms a collection of findings in which, over time, identify trends or patterns for a larger population. The examples illustrate the dimensions of scientific criteria and confirm that it is not an all-or-nothing type of approach. Hence, an appreciation can be gained for researchers' ingenuity and perseverance that bestow the qualities of inquiry and curiosity. Those qualities are necessary to push forward the boundaries of human knowledge and for that knowledge to be accepted by the scientific community and society at-large.

Refresher

Science seeks to explain natural phenomena and follows a systematic methodology or scientific method. The scientific community agrees on what qualifies as scientific according to certain criteria: the principle of falsifiability, empirical evidence, and reproducibility. These criteria are embedded in the scientific method and strengthen the reliability and validity of experimentation. Research applies the scientific method to explain phenomenon. The research cycle guides the process of how findings are reached and disseminated through the process of peer review. Research branches into several types, and the practice of research is pursued from different interests that include academia, government, or private institutions. Although most people would argue that science must meet certain criteria, there is a certain dimension to science that can be stretched to other approaches that seek to unravel unexplained phenomenon. History has taught us that pursuing scientific quests has always been met with opposition, but those that believe in searching for truths must press on, and eventually their voices are heard and accepted.

End-of-Chapter Exercises: Applying Concepts

The following passages describe a research approach to explain a phenomenon. Is the approach scientific? Answer the questions below:

Summary One:

Danny is an undergraduate in a chemistry laboratory. He is testing the effectiveness of a compound "X" to trap bacteria. Danny first measures the concentration of the bacteria using a spectrophotometer. The spectrophotometer reading indicates a 0.1 value, which corresponds to a bacterial concentration of 8×10^8 cells/ml. Danny fills a 10-ml vial with 5 ml of compound "X" diluted in sterile saline. Then he adds the bacterial concentration to the 10-ml vial containing the 5-ml compound "X" in saline. He covers the vial and sets it on the counter overnight in a sterile area. After 24 hours, Danny removes 1 ml from the 10-ml vial containing the bacteria and compound "X." He again measures the bacterial concentration using the spectrophotometer. The reading is a .01, which translates to a concentration of 8×10^6 cells/ml.

Danny reports that his first reading before exposing the bacteria to compound "X" was 8×10^8 cells/ml. Twenty-four hours after the bacteria were mixed in with compound "X," the bacterial concentration was 8×10^6 cells/ml. Danny claims that there was a decrease in bacterial concentration after exposing the bacteria to compound "X." Therefore, compound "X" trapped the bacteria.

1. Does Danny's research approach meet the criteria of
    a. empirical evidence? Explain.
    b. reproducibility? Explain.
    c. the principle of falsifiability? Explain.
    d. Based on your answers for a, b, and c, would Danny's work be considered science? Explain.
2. If a criterion was answered no, what could Danny do to meet that criterion?

Summary Two:

Jill likes to work out at the gym three times a week. She goes to the gym on Mondays (Mon.), Wednesdays (Wed.), and Fridays (Fri.), and has frequented the gym for over a year consistently on those days. On one occasion, Jill goes to the gym on Saturday (Sat.) and observes that people at the gym appear to be fitter than the gym-goers that she sees on Mon., Wed., and Fri. Jill decides to test if people that work out at that gym on Saturdays are more fit than individuals that go to that gym on other days of the week. Jill shows up to that gym Mon. through Sat. between 6 a.m. to 8 a.m. for three months and logs her observations. Using the logged information, she concludes that Sat. gym-goers are more fit than those who go on other weekdays.

1. Does Jill's research approach meet the criteria of
   a. empirical evidence? Explain.
   b. reproducibility? Explain.
   c. the principle of falsifiability? Explain.
   d. Based on your answers for a, b, and c, would Jill's work be considered science? Explain.
2. If the criterion above was answered no, what could Jill do to meet that criterion?

References

Fornshell, J. A., & Tesei, A. (2013). The development of SONAR as a tool in marine biological research in the twentieth century. *International Journal of Oceanography, 2013,* 1-9. doi:10.1155/2013/678621

Gibney, E. (2015). Injectable brain implant spies on individual neurons. *Nature News, 522*(7555), 137-138. doi:10.1038/522137a

Chapter 3: Experimental Design

"In the field of observation, chance favors only the prepared mind."

–Louis Pasteur

Learning Objectives:

1. Describe the different types of studies.
2. Define the differences between true and quasi-experimental design.
3. Explain the research cycle.

Why are models used to inform about the human condition?

Introduction

Experimental design is at the heart of research, and through carefully crafted experiments, questions can be answered with a degree of precision. In research, a number of approaches can be pursued to address a problem or question. How do researchers decide which approach is best? The approach rests on the researcher's interests and, also, the *research discipline* may dictate the approach. The researcher may be a professional in academia, in the medical field, in the government, or in the private sector. For example, a researcher may be interested in how organisms expend energy, more formally referred to as the *mechanisms of metabolic function*. Metabolic function is an extensive area of study that encompasses the whole organism down to the microscopic level. Furthermore, metabolic function can be studied in humans or through the use of models. Models are highly relied upon to gain information about other organisms, especially humans.

The Use of Models in Research

Models refer to the ability to use a nonhuman organism to study a phenomenon that may resemble the function and structure of humans or other organisms. Experiments that use models most often take place in the laboratory setting under well-controlled conditions. Models can be small animals (e.g., rodents), large animals (e.g., primates), insects (e.g., flies or worms), and cell organisms (e.g., bacteria). Models can also be in the form of technology (e.g., computer programming). Why can models be used when the questions that are asked are about humans? The use of models rests in the belief that if a phenomenon is true, then that phenomenon will also be true in an organism that shares similar physiology, cellular and chemical structure, and will function as that of a human. To adequately model a phenomenon, the models must resemble the symptomatology of the condition that is studied. Researchers have developed models of human diseases, for example, neurodegenerative diseases (e.g., Parkinson's disease, Alzheimer's disease, or multiple sclerosis) that help to explain the mental and physical human condition. The researcher decides which model works best with the available resources at hand.

Animal-model research follows levels of experimentation that start from the simplest organism to the more complex ones. These levels of testing are exemplified in drug development research in which the testing goes through phases that start with insects or small animals. If the drug shows promise in the smaller organisms, then the next phase of testing may involve primates. This experimentation continues to the next phase, and if the drug continues to show promise, i.e., the drug benefits outweigh the risks, that drug moves forward to clinical trials where testing is done with humans. Once the testing reaches human trials, then phases of experimentation again take place before the drug is approved for the public or the market. The process of drug testing described involves researchers with expertise in drug development using small-animal models to experts with primate research experience and finally to researchers that are licensed to perform clinical trials with patients.

Diseases that are inflicted by bacteria or viruses are most commonly studied using models. Infectious disease research can involve humans under certain circumstances. For example, in 2014, the outbreak of Ebola in West Africa resulted in endemic infections putting the medical staff the local population at risk. A couple of the U.S health workers were exposed and infected with the Ebola virus while working at the Centers for Disease Control and Prevention (Centers for Disease Control and Prevention, 2014). An experimental vaccine, ZMAPP, although tested in primates, had not previously been tested in humans and was administered to the healthcare workers infected with the Ebola virus (Enserink, 2014). Fortunately, the vaccine was very effective and the workers' health was restored. The extraordinary circumstances of the Ebola outbreak of 2014 justified the use of an experimental vaccine that was not ready for human trials. These types of cases are rare. (Historical unethical cases that involved humans and animals are discussed in the Ethics chapter.)

Technological models have assisted researchers in learning about the human condition, marine life, and other organisms. Additionally, technology has benefited greatly in learning about the phenomenon of outer space and Earth. The use of technology in environmental science is aiding scientists in deciphering the impact of pollution on climate change. Climate change research is under intense scrutiny and has become a political debate mainly because of rising global temperatures and the thinning of the ozone layer that scientists claim are consequences of human actions and less about what some argue are causes of natural climate changes (Parson, 2010).

Types of Studies

Descriptive Studies

Studies that involve collecting data, which inform about specific characteristics of a population, are known as *descriptive*. Descriptive studies provide information about the frequency of an occurrence. Also, from this type of study, patterns or commonalities within a population can be picked up. Descriptive studies rely on data that is readily available. An instructor interested in the classroom students' sociodemographics such as age, gender, and major can readily collect that data by asking the students to provide such information. The instructor can categorize the data by gender, i.e., male or female, and organize the data by age and major. With the data collected, the teacher can determine information about the demographics of the students in the classroom, such as which majors are most common, the male-to-female ratio, and the students' average age.

Case Studies

In certain occasions, usual circumstances require the necessity to document and report. Such a report is considered a case study because the information comes from only one case. Case studies are standard in medical reports in which doctors document rare cases that deviate from the average patient pool. A physician may treat a patient with a rare disease for which no record exists in the medical archives. The physician can report such findings as a case study delineating the symptoms, treatment, and prognosis of the rare disease; that record then becomes part of the medical archives. Case studies are also common in the social sciences; for example, a psychologist may report on the progress of an individual that is recovering from drug addiction and undergoing a new rehabilitative program. Although the information provided from case studies contribute significantly to the existing literature, these reports may not necessarily be reproducible. In most situations, case studies may be evaluated to identify similarities between case studies by compiling the data to potentially form a new classification of a disorder, disease, or syndrome. The beginning of the HIV-infection epidemic in the early 1980s, when patients presented with symptoms in which the cause of those symptoms was not yet known to be HIV, resulted in countless case studies. These case studies provided sufficient information that helped the medical field categorize similarities among the cases that led to identifying an immune deficiency, creating a nomenclature that evolved into the acquired immune deficiency syndrome or AIDS. Because adult cases were different from that of child cases, further classification of AIDS evolved to differentiate between adult and child symptomatology. As cases were presented over time, the classification of AIDS continued to evolve (Caldwell, Oxtoby, Simonds, Lindegren, & Rogers, 1994).

Studies with Controlled Conditions

True Experiments

True experiments primarily take place in a laboratory setting where most of the experimental conditions are artificial and controlled. The experimental design includes an experimental variable or key variable whose effects will result in a predicted outcome. Because the experimental variable is subject to change or can be manipulated, this variable is referred to as the *independent variable*. The variable that is the measurable observation and contingent upon the independent variable is the *dependent variable*. The dependent variable cannot be manipulated; rather, it is subject to change according to the independent (experimental) variable. For example, an instructor wishes to test the effects of two different lesson plans of the same topic on students' grades and performance. The independent variable is the lesson plan because the instructor can assign different lesson plans to students in which no one student receives both lesson plans. The grade is the dependent variable because it is the measurable observation or output of the experiment that is not subject to change or manipulation. The instructor can control variables such as the students' ages and genders to form groups that are similar; for instance, only those students that are between the age of 18 and 19 are included, and either males or females are included. Isolating the variables helps to minimize the factors that may introduce effects of their own, which may interfere with or confound the effects of the independent variable, i.e., the lesson plan.

True experimental designs also factor in the environmental conditions where the experiment takes place, known as *controlled conditions*. In the lesson plan comparison experiment, the instructor can control conditions such as the temperature of the room, the seating arrangements, and the noise level. These conditions must be maintained in the same manner during the experiment. In experiments that involve animal models, the animals' housing, temperature, sleep and/or wake cycles, and feeding schedules are the controlled conditions. True experimental designs are limited in extrapolating findings because the experimental conditions may not apply outside the laboratory setting. However, these stringent conditions isolate the effects of the independent variable that allows for well-controlled experimentation. True experiments are advantageous because of the well-controlled conditions that are reproducible, which strengthen the reliability and validity of the results. In cases where variables cannot be changed, other experimental designs are then more appropriate.

Quasi-Experimental Design

Quasi-experimental designs are appropriate when certain variables or conditions of the experiment cannot be controlled. Quasi-experiments are most applicable in studies that involve drug addicts, pregnant women, prisoners, and the mentally ill. For example, studies that seek to investigate the effectiveness of a withdrawal intervention program for drug addicts are quasi-experiments. These studies are quasi-experiments (partly) as a result of several constraints: 1) the researcher cannot "create" addictive behavior to then test the effectiveness of an intervention program; and 2) the variability introduced by the participant's history of drug addiction poses a threat to the validity of the results because the variable (drug addiction) may confound the effects of the intervention plan. Although confounds may be present with quasi-experimental design, this type of design allows for the gathering of information that cannot be created in a true experiment setting.

Cross-Sectional and Longitudinal Experimental Designs

The decision to design an experiment with one or more time-point measurements, again, depends on the researcher's question. A design that involves only one time-point is a *cross-sectional* design. This type of study can take a few hours or even days but is only contingent upon the outcome of the one time-point. Cross-sectional studies primarily take place in a laboratory setting using models, e.g., animal or insect. Experimental designs that require more than one time-point, which span the course of months or years, even decades, are referred to as *longitudinal*. Longitudinal studies examine the long-term effects of a particular variable and are common in experiments that involve humans or large animals. In addition, this type of study is adequate for studies of space missions or environmental changes, e.g., climate change.

Qualitative and Quantitative Research

Qualitative Data

Researchers must consider what type of data is appropriate for their designs. Data can be *qualitative* or *quantitative* and, in some cases are both. Distinctive differences exist between these two types of data. Qualitative data are subjective and not easily measured. Studies that try to measure emotions, e.g., happiness, or physiological states, e.g., pain, are of a qualitative nature. How do researchers attempt to measure emotions, i.e., happiness, or physiological states, i.e., pain? The researcher assigns an *operational definition* to the variable to attribute characteristics that define the variable. For example, the operational definition of happiness may include smiling, laughing, or giggling. Any one of these signs of expression defines happiness. Keep in mind that exhibiting these characteristics can only infer happiness; a researcher cannot know for sure that happiness is experienced when smiling. However, most would agree that laughing is characteristic of someone experiencing happiness. Operationalizing variables permits objective measurements. Also, qualitative variables can be measured on a rating scale, such as a Likert scale, which is often used to transform a qualitative measure into a numerical value. This type of scale is usually a 5- to 7-point scale that ranges from 1, least likely (strongly disagree), to 5 (or 7), most likely (strongly agree), with a neutral point at the center. If an individual is asked to mark the point on the scale that reflects how happy he or she feels at that moment, then that emotion can be objectified. Ambiguities exist in qualitative measurements because it relies on self-reports that are subject to the interpretation of the person who rates him- or herself. A variable that is described or measured according to the intensity or magnitude it exhibits is also of a qualitative nature. Consider measuring genetic material or DNA that is invisible to the naked eye. A researcher adds dye to a DNA sample to allow viewing of the genetic material. With specialized equipment, the genetic material forms a visible band. The intensity and magnitude (or size) of the band indirectly provides an estimate of the concentration of the DNA. Although the DNA bands may provide information in the broader sense based on magnitude and intensity, this type of measurement is always compared with a known concentration that acts as the control. Researchers' interpretations are limited when the measurements are qualitative.

Methodology of Qualitative Research

Qualitative research can take place in the form of interviews or focus groups. For example, when an instructor wants a student's input on a particular lesson, the instructor may interview students independently and ask questions about their perceptions of the lesson plan in a one-to-one setting. Or, the instructor can gather a few students to form a focus group in which indivdiuals are asked a question and then allowed to continue the conversation while the researcher jots down words or phrases. If students were asked how they perceived a particular lesson plan, they may start by describing how they felt about it, such as, "I felt it was challenging." The instructor clusters the students' comments that resonate the same topic or *theme*. The students' comments make reference to material content and their motivations. The themes, hence, are labeled "Content of Material" and "Motivation to Learn" with the students' statements listed under the corresponding theme (Figure 3.1). Qualitative data, either collected from interviews or focus groups, allows open-ended answers that can lead to new information. However, the subjective nature of qualitative data can be problematic to reproducibility and precision, which sacrifices reliability and the validity of analyses.

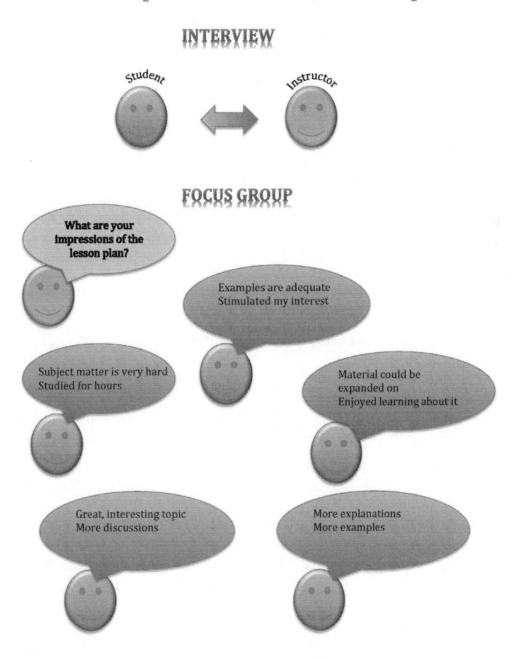

Figure 3.1: Qualitative research: Interview versus focus group.

Interview: The instructor (green) asks about the students' (blue) perception of the lesson plan. Focus group: A group of students comment on the instructor's questions about the lesson plan. The students' statements are clustered into *themes (table, below)*

Table 3.1. Themes

THEMES:	Content of Material	Motivation to Learn
	• Examples are adequate	• Enjoyed learning about it
	• More explanation	• Great, interesting topic
	• More examples	• Subject matter very hard
	• More discussions	• Stimulated my interest
	• Material could be expanded upon	• Studied for hours

Quantitative Data

Quantitative data is numerical with precise measurements or is attained from accurate estimations. Height, temperature, and weight are a few examples of quantitative data. In the previous section, DNA concentrations were determined through qualitative means. Advances in biotechnology have made it possible to quantify DNA with a high level of precision. Equipment such as the real-time polymerase chain-reaction (RT-PCR or quantitative PCR) machine can count the base pairs of DNA after the DNA has been amplified or replicated several times. The advantage of quantitative data is that it strengthens the reliability and validity of experimentation.

Methodology of Quantitative Research

Researchers that require quantitative measures for their experimental designs can use descriptive or *inferential data*. In contrast to descriptive data, inferential data is not readily available; therefore, this data informs about a population based on data collected from a sample. By and large, quantitative analyses are applicable to true or quasi-experimental designs. The example of the instructor who wanted to learn about the difference between students' performances on two lesson plans may assign a quiz that covers the material of the lesson plans. In this situation, the quantitative measurement is the quiz grade. The instructor can then compare class performance differences between the two lesson plans.

The Experimental Process

Developing the Background

How does the novel researcher start the experimental process? The novel researcher begins with an interest in a particular research topic; for example, how does diabetes develop in children? Topics on diabetes are extensive, therefore narrowing the topic brings focus and helps sleuth through the vast amount of available information. It takes years to become well-versed in a specific area of research to qualify a person as an expert. The novel researcher can refer to the scientific literature and learn about the topic of interest. (See Chapter 5: Scientific Literature more information about scientific literature). A wealth of scientific literature is available that can guide the novice in identifying or narrowing his or her chosen topic. Once settled on a topic, the process begins with selecting scientific literature based on what is known about the topic. As the novel researcher searches the literature, what is not known about that topic becomes clearer. In the event that the novel researcher is actively engaged in a research project and obtains unexpected findings, referring to the scientific literature will also help interpret the results. The novel researcher should document the key findings from the scientific literature as well as document inconsistencies from the literature sources. The inconsistencies in the literature indicate that there are gaps that remain to be filled. These gaps of information can lead to forming *research questions*.

Developing Research Questions

The research question must be original and seek to explain a new phenomenon. Also, the question can address an existing gap in the scientific literature. Research questions are specific and should identify what the researcher wants to measure.

Sample research questions

Marine Biology: Have Steller's eider offspring decreased in number during the past decade?

The number of offspring is a quantitative measure.

Sociology: Do teens' attitudes toward school change if they are involved in after-school programs?

Because the question seeks to measure teens' attitudes, then a qualitative research approach is most appropriate in this case.

Framing the Hypothesis Statement

Contrary to the research question, a hypothesis is a statement. However, the research question and the hypothesis are the same. The hypothesis, also referred to as the *research hypothesis* or *alternative hypothesis*, makes a prediction of a specific outcome.

Although the hypothesis predicts a specific outcome, the design of the experiment must have an element that can "disconfirm" the prediction or *falsifiability* (see Chapter 2: Defining Science). A statement can be formulated that contradicts the research hypothesis statement, referred to as the *null hypothesis*, which states that no change will occur as a result of any manipulation of the independent variable. Therefore, it is a zero (null) outcome or effect.

Consider the following analogy to help conceptualize the research and null hypothesis: In the court of law, an individual accused of a crime is believed "innocent until proven guilty."

The burden on the prosecution side is to provide sufficient evidence against the accused, i.e., without reasonable doubt the accused will be proven guilty. But, if any doubt is introduced in the testimony that questions the guilty charge, the accused must be acquitted of the charges and presumed not guilty. Therefore, guilty and not guilty can be represented as:

Research hypothesis: Guilty

Null hypothesis: Not Guilty

In the same line, the research hypothesis for the two research questions above can be stated as follows:

Research hypothesis:

The number of Steller's eider offspring has decreased in the past decade.

Null hypothesis:

The number of Steller's eider offspring has not decreased in the past decade.

Research hypothesis:

Teens' attitudes toward school do change when involved in after-school programs.

Null hypothesis:

Teens' attitudes toward school do not change when involved in after-school programs.

The sample hypotheses state a prediction because the research hypothesis predicts a specific outcome, and that outcome is contradicted by the null hypothesis.

The Development of Experimental Design

Designing experiments is much like searching for a specific light switch in a dark room filled with impeding objects and many other light switches. The researcher must create a strategy to arrive at the correct light switch that will shine light on the truth about a phenomenon. An example of searching to shine light on unknown phenomena is the time when people believed that organisms originated from nothing, or spontaneous generation. This belief was much debated until Louis Pasteur, a scientist who is regarded as one of the first multidisciplinary scientists, put the debate to rest. Louis Pasteur's keen observations debunked the theory of spontaneous generation (Nicolle, 1961). This historical anecdote describes the simplicity of Pasteur's design in which he brilliantly applied his previous knowledge about germs and his observations of others' experiments. He filled several glass flasks with equal amounts of a liquid. The composition of the liquid was prepared with ingredients that microorganisms feed on for nourishment, helping the organisms to propagate. After adding the liquid, he modified the openings of the flasks to stretch outward forming longnecks with a bent end at the opening that resembled spoons. All of the ends of the necks were left open. Half of the flasks were sterilized with heat, and the other flasks were left unheated. Thereafter, the flasks were left untouched for a period of time. Upon inspection of the flasks after this period, he made the observation that growth was visible in the unheated flasks but no growth was evident in the heated flasks. It was under these controlled conditions, modification of the flasks, heat or no heat conditions, along with a few ensuing other experiments that a strong case was made that organisms were carried in the air and settled on surfaces. Additionally, he found that if the passage of air into the flasks was impeded, the entry of organisms in the flasks was also impeded. Louis Pasteur's experimental design, which was based on his previous knowledge and analytical thinking, led him to his evidence and disconfirmed the phenomenon of spontaneous generation.

Predictions

In all true- and quasi-experimental designs, hypothesis-driven research has a specific outcome. In a well-controlled experiment, predictions can be made that help narrow the possible outcomes of an experiment. For example, Louis Pasteur predicted that organismal growth would be evident in unsealed containers because the organisms were from the air and not originated from nothing, i.e., spontaneously generated. His conditions (i.e., flasks that contained liquid, were exposed to air before modifying the openings, and heated or not heated) tested his prediction. However, other outcomes were possible: 1) all of the flasks (heated and unheated) could show organismal growth; 2) only the unheated flasks could show organismal growth; and 3) none of the flasks could show organismal growth. Pasteur's design allowed his predicted outcome to be tested, but in the event his predicted outcome was a null effect, a limited number of other possible outcomes were possible. If the possible outcomes of an experiment can be predicted, then a well-controlled experiment was achieved. If countless outcomes are possible from an experiment, then refinement of the controlled conditions must be done to narrow the possible outcomes.

Alternative Explanations

When an outcome is not what was predicted, but another of the possible outcomes occurs, the researcher is tasked with explaining the other outcome(s). It turns out that Louis Pasteur noted from one of his experiments that no growth developed in some of the unheated flasks and he speculated that on that occasion the air was not contaminated with organisms. Other alternative explanations that may have been considered were that the organisms were not viable when in contact with the liquid, or that they lacked sufficient nourishment to reproduce, and consequently died. These alternative explanations could also explain the absence of organismal growth.

The process of understanding the literature to help develop research questions, then forming hypotheses that can then be tested through experimentation, is part of the research cycle. The cycle continues with alternative explanations for outcomes that are unexpected. When the hypothesized outcome is the result, new questions inevitably arise. These new questions form the *next logical step*, which follows a line of reason that extends from the previously acquired knowledge. For example, in one of Pasteur's experiments in support of his theory that the organisms were suspended in air, he placed open flasks in an open space where the air was undisturbed. He wished to demonstrate that in still-air conditions, no organismal growth would be observed inside the flasks. In doing so and in his subsequent experimentation, Louis Pasteur was following the next logical step in his reasoning.

Refresher

A number of research approaches are possible for pursuing unexplained phenomenon. The researchers' interests and disciplines will primarily guide the approach that is pursued. Irrespective of the type of research or the approach, the experiment design is at the heart of the research process, which dictates the level of reliability and validity invested in the results. Insects, animals, and technology are useful as models to gain knowledge about complex organisms such as humans. The type of study that researchers choose is dependent upon the accessibility of data: Data can be either readily accessible, which can be descriptive, or inferential, which is derived from samples that inform about populations. Some experimentation is best in a laboratory setting, where well-controlled conditions made possible though these types of experiments are limited when applied to settings outside the laboratory. In circumstances where certain variables cannot be changed, then quasi-experiments are fitting. Studies can be cross-sectional or longitudinal. Data can be of a qualitative or quantitative nature depending on the type of questions asked. In most cases, research follows a systematic approach that initiates with building a background of knowledge about a specific research interest. A well-read literature background helps formulate research questions. The research questions address gaps that exist in the literature or questions that arise from observations made while carrying out experiments. From these research questions, hypothesis statements that can then be tested with experiments are formed. Experiments must be designed with the goal of testing the predicted outcome. The possible outcomes must be reasonable in number, otherwise the experimental design requires refinement. In the event that the predicted outcome is not the result, alternative explanations must be offered and reasonable explanations provided that can guide the next questions or the next logical step.

End-of-Chapter Exercises: Applying Concepts

1. Determine which of the following are qualitative, quantitative, or both.
   A. Pain level
   B. DNA base pairs
   C. Satisfaction of treatment at a restaurant
   D. Yearly lunar phases
   E. Responses of a drug addict in reply to level of discomfort after abstaining from drug intake
   F. Evaluation of employees' job performances

2. For each of the following indicate if a true or quasi-experimental design is most appropriate, and explain why.
   A. A clinician is interested in learning if a novel vaccine that has been approved for clinical trials will be effective in treating HIV.
   B. A professor is interested in the effects of a drug for alleviating pain.
   C. A marketing company seeks to learn if one of their makeup products sells more in an area with less televised marketing.
   D. The government is invested in learning whether treating soldiers with biofeedback will help alleviate their post-traumatic stress experiences.

References

Caldwell, B. M., Oxtoby, M. J., Simonds, R. J., Lindegren, M., & Rogers, M. F. (1994). *1994 revised classification system for human immunodeficiency virus infection in children less than 13 years of age.* Centers for Disease Control, Division of HIV/AIDS National Center for Infectious Diseases. Atlanta: CDC.

Centers for Disease Control and Prevention. (2014). Retrieved from https://www.cdc.gov/vhf/ebola/outbreaks/2014-west-africa/united-states-imported-case.html

Enserink, M. (2014). How two U.S. patients changed the debate about using untested Ebola drugs. *Science.* Retrieved from http://www.sciencemag.org/news/2014/08/how-two-us-patients-changed-debate-about-using-untested-ebola-drugs

Nicolle, J. (1961). *Louis Pasteur: The story of his major discoveries.* New York: Basic Books.

Parson, E. A. (2010). *The science and politics of global climate change: A guide to the debate* (2nd ed.). (A. E. Dessler, & E. A. Parson, Eds.) Cambridge: Cambridge University Press.

Chapter 4: Basic Statistics

"Statistics may be defined as 'a body of methods for making wise decisions in the face of uncertainty.'"

–Wilson Allen Wallis

Learning Objectives:

1. Explain how statistics are applied.
2. Explain measures of centrality and distribution.
3. Interpret graphical representation of data.
4. Explain the limitations of statistics.

What reasoning is applied in choosing the statistical significance level?

Introduction

Statistics provide information about natural phenomena when using this tool effectively; therefore, step-by-step explanations with examples are provided so that the reader can follow and understand how statistics are used in research. The topics covered, although not exhaustive, are identifying a population from a sample, selecting the appropriate measure of centrality and distribution, and identifying outliers. Also included are topics of how statistics are applied to hypotheses testing in the context of setting a level of significance, the type of errors that can be committed when making decisions about the hypothesis (reject or fail to reject the Ho), and interpreting statistical outputs.

What are statistics, and how are they used? Statistics are a tool that is used to corroborate a belief that an event or phenomenon exists or occurs in the natural world. Statistics are to provide information about a population from a sample data set. The information statistics provide is the probability of an occurrence happening in the population. Statistics can be illustrated numerically and graphically.

Principle of Falsifiability Example

The *principle of falsifiability* is a criterion in scientific methodology that rests on the idea that hypotheses must be "disproved" to minimize bias. Consider this example of how the principle of falsifiability applies: A hypothetical scenario in which two friends that meet each other on a daily basis for three consecutive years and each time these two friends meet, one of them is always wearing an orange shirt. The other friend, the observer, makes note that the friend has worn an orange shirt for the past three years, or 1,095 days and other colored shirts, zero days. Therefore, the observer predicts or hypothesizes that the friend only owns orange-colored shirts. However, on day 1,096, the observer notices that the friend shows up wearing a blue shirt. This one occasion that the friend wore a different colored shirt was sufficient to disprove the observer's prediction. The observer cannot affirm with 100% certainty that the other person did not own other colored clothes just because orange was the only colored shirt the observer had witnessed on a daily basis for over three years. It is plausible that the friend had that blue shirt (and possibly other colored shirts) but had not worn it during the times the two met. The fact that the observer had not witnessed the friend wearing anything else but orange shirts does not "prove" the friend only owned orange shirts is an affirmation of the principle of falsifiability. In the following context, explanations are given as to how statistics are used to underscorethe principle of falsifiability in testing hypotheses.

Before pre-statistical software was available, analyzing data could take days, weeks or months but with today's technological advances, researchers can analyze large datasets in no time. However, the ease and accessibility of statistical software can be a double- edged sword for the novice because it is easy to use the statistical software without the conceptual foundation as to how the statistics are applied, consequently data may be misinterpreted. How does the novice get started when dealing with data? Before gathering data and analyzing it, the *population* of interest is first identified and the characteristic(s) or *variable*(s) of that population is used to select the appropriate statistical approach.

Populations and Samples

In *experimentation,* a population does not have to refer to people. It can be anything that will be studied. For example, a population can apply to animals, vegetation, or microorganisms. It is the rare case when data can be collected from an entire population. For example, during the census people go door to door to inquire how many individuals live in a household. The task of visiting households is a worldwide effort, and although efforts are made to reach every place that people may inhabit, it is impossible to reach all the homes in the world or witness all of the individuals within one household. Although an arduous effort, a large amount of data is collected. Statisticians categorize the data and use algorithms to estimate the number of people in the world, which is estimated to be 7.3 billion (U.S. and World Population Clock, 2017). However, it is more realistic and plausible to select a population that is more focused, such as the residents of a small city. Even when the population is from a small city, collecting data from all of the residents may be difficult. For instance, if the Centers for Disease Control and Prevention (CDC) requires knowing how many cases of flu occurred in a previous year, the only information the CDC can collect is from hospitals or doctors visits. Those flu cases that resolve on their own without some record or confirmation that it was a flu case are unaccountable. If the desired information of a population is not available because of inaccessibility or limited funding, then a sample from the population is appropriate. The process of selecting a sample should meet certain conditions. A sample should be randomly selected to ensure that the population is well-represented in that sample. Samples can be stratified in which subgroups are formed, and from those subgroups the samples are randomly selected. For example, stratified sampling can involve choosing men and women that serve in the various military branches, and from that group these men and women are randomly selected to determine the years of service for each military branch. Sampling can occur in an interval manner when dealing with large populations. If conducting a survey at a mall to learn about shoppers' habits during Christmas, then sampling may include every 5th person that walks by to have a more efficient and random selection. *Matched* sampling is more challenging compared with other samples because the matched samples must match exactly, with the exception of the variable of interest to be tested. Identical twin studies are ideal for matched samples because of their identical genetic makeup. A prominent identical twin study of the 21st century is that of Scott and Mark Kelly, the famous astronauts. The identical twins are the first to be part of an identical twin study conducted by NASA to learn how genes are affected after prolonged periods in space (Gushanas, 2017). Scott has recently returned from a near-year-long space mission in which he was based at the International Space Station. Mark was on Earth with the rest of us. Scott and Mark's genes are presently being analyzed to determine if genetic differences exist between the two identical twin's genes.

Parameters and Statistics

Measurements that describe a variable or variables about a population are called *parameters*. Parameters inform of the average (or mean; *mu* or "μ") and standard deviation (the average spread of variables from the mean, sigma or "σ") of a population. Statistics apply to samples to infer information about a population. The statistics for mean and standard deviation are designated with $\bar{x}$ (*x bar*) and the letter S (or SD), respectively. As an example, education policymakers may be interested in the income of the educators, administrators, and students from a particular elementary school. If yearly income data of all the educators, administrators and, students is available, then the population parameters, μ and σ, can be calculated to obtain the yearly income mean and distribution. However, if the income is not accessible, then a random sample drawn from educators, administrators, and students can be selected to obtain the yearly income. Then the sample statistics $\bar{x}$ and S can infer the average and distribution for the income level of that specific elementary school's population.

Data can be descriptive when the data is readily available. Inferential statistics provide information that is not readily available about a specific population's variable(s), therefore the information is inferred. Descriptive statistics summarize data or describe the frequency of a variable. For example, descriptive statistics can refer to the number of phones purchased by individuals of varying ages. A frequency table can be used to designate age blocks of 20 years (0–20, 21–40, 41–60, and 61–80). By summing the numbers that fall under each age block, the frequency of phone purchases according to age is easy to discern. In the case of phone purchases, global sales data is not accessible; a stratified sample can be picked from different countries and then randomly selected to obtain the mean, $\bar{x}$, and distribution of that sample, S. That $\bar{x}$ and S for phone purchases are estimates of the parameters of the population, or μ and σ phone purchases. Descriptive statistics would suffice to determine frequency of phone purchases of a known population; however, in the absense of available data estimates of global sales can be derived with more sophisticated inferential analyses.

Choosing a Population

How is a population chosen or narrowed down? This question depends on what specific information or variable of a particular population is of interest. For example, mobile phone companies, such as Apple or Samsung, are invested in learning the *sociodemographics* of individuals that buy their phones: Are these people adults, are they employed, are they males or females, do they reside in similar areas, and are they low or high income? These companies have expert statisticians that can perform sophisticated analyses using a company's revenue to determine how many phones are purchased and which sociodemographic is common to those who buy their phones. In the example above, the phone companies invest in searching for factors that motivate individuals to purchase phones, such as income level or ease of use of the phone. In contrast, if a researcher is interested in the efficacy of a drug that may alleviate Alzheimer's disease symptoms, the population of interest is individuals that have Alzheimer's. However, it is not possible to test the drug on all the Alzheimer's-afflicted individuals around the world. Therefore, a *sample* from a population of individuals that have Alzheimer's can be tested to make *inferences* about the efficacy of the drug on alleviating Alzheimer's symptoms. In the event that the drug is in its early stages of testing, a researcher will use an animal model, i.e., mice with Alzheimer's disease. The population of interest and variable in the three examples are people that buy phones, people with Alzheimer's disease to test the efficacy of a drug, and an animal model of Alzheimer's disease, in this case mice, to also test the efficacy of a drug (see Chapter 6: Ethics in Research for more on animal models).

A Population Example

Cell phones have become a utility of global dimension in which individuals are always engaged in some form of communication using their cell phones. There are several mobile phone choices from which to choose provoking competition among the phone conglomerates. Apple's research team is invested in gathering iPhone sales compared with that of other phones such as Androids (this example is not to advocate purchasing iPhones or Androids). To address the question of whether most people prefer iPhones compared with Android phones, the population of interest is first defined. A population of interest can be everyone around the world. It is most feasible that the research team would be interested in individuals from a specific region, maybe from one particular country, a city, and/or a particular group of people of a certain age in which the population is significantly narrowed down. The population of interest may be undergraduates between the ages of 17 to 28 that are attending a four-year university ("Excel University" in this example) located in a region of a particular yearly household income level (Figure 4.1). This specific population is accessible and large enough to gather a sample and collect data for the desired measures, $\bar{x}$ and S.

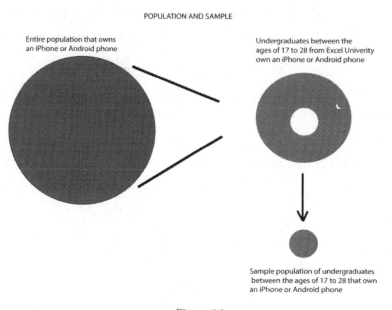

Figure 4.1

Measures of Centrality

Imagine a pendulum swinging back and forth until it stops at the center; similarly, measures of centrality focus on the center. The three measures of centrality are the mode, median, and mean. In Apple's theoretical study, the research team may be interested in whether age is a factor that differs between those that prefer iPhone to Android phones. Before conducting statistical analyses, it is always good practice to organize the variables, e.g., age in ascending order for each set of data or groups (Figure 4.2). By ordering the data in chronological order, several pieces of information are obtained: 1) the *mode,* 2) the *median,* and 3) *outliers.* If the team wishes to learn what the most common age is that comprises each group, then the mode is the appropriate measure. The mode is the most frequent variable in the dataset (Figure 4.2). The point that marks half of the data that fall below and above that point is the median (Figure 4.2). The average, unlike the median, is sensitive to low or high values and can be used to determine *statistical significances.* The average is the sum of the variables and divided by the total number of samples that comprise the variables of the group (Figure 4.3).

Undergraduates' age that either preferred an iphone or Android

iPhone	21	17	19	23	25	22	18	19	18	18	28	20	21	19	17
Android	17	20	24	24	25	20	24	23	25	23	19	18	22	19	27

iPhone	17	17	**18**	**18**	**18**	**18**	18	**19**	19	20	21	21	23	25	28
Android	17	18	19	19	20	21	22	**22**	23	24	24	**25**	**25**	**25**	27

Figure 4.2

Measurement Scales

Data can be categorized into one of four scales depending of the type of data. The measurement scale that is used depends on the information the data provides. Nominal data includes data that can be labeled or categorized such as names of football teams, shades of color, or gender.

This data cannot be ranked in an increasing or decreasing order. Data that can be organized from low to high or vice versa is known as ordinal data which can be classified according to level such as the ranking of football teams' season performances. Also, classifications of occupational positions can be ordinal data such as military rank. Subjective data such as emotional states (happy, unhappy) can be ordered from least likely to most likely or highly disagree to highly agree. An ordinal scale is appropriate for data that disregard or do not have any significance for any value between the data; for example, top ten football season performances listed from best = 1 to least = 10, or grades, A, B, C, D, or F. There is no such thing as a 1½ best football season performance or a B½, right? A scale that does factor in between values is appropriately called interval data. With interval data, however, the value of zero does not take any significant value. Temperature is an interval value because there is such a thing as 98.1° F through 98.9° F. However, a temperature of 0 °F does not mean that there is an absence of temperature, in fact, a 0 °-F temperature means a certain degree in Fahrenheit and a different temperature in Celsius (32° C) or Kelvin (273° K).

Some data can be classified under different scales. Ratio data is similar to interval data, except that the value of zero does have significance. Measures of height, weight, and age are ratio scales. With ratio values, unlike interval scales, the difference between values, such as 5, 10, 15, 20, and 25 have significance. Someone who is ten years old is twice as old as a 5-year-old.

Certain measurements can be more than one scale for example time. If measuring time in seconds, minutes, hours, or years, then a ratio scale can apply because the value zero has significance and the values between the data also have meaning. However, if time is ranked from an earlier to a later period such as years, 1920, 1950, 1980, and 2010, then an ordinal scale applies. If the number between the years is the measure, then an interval scale can be assigned. The measurement of the data will determine the designation of the scale for the dataset.

Measures of centrality, e.g., the mode, median, and average can be designated to different measurement scales. The mode can be designated to nominal, ordinal, interval, and ratio data. The median can also be applied to ordinal, interval, and ratio data but not nominal data. The mean can be designated to interval and ratio data and can be applied to nominal data if converted to numerical values or *coded*, i.e., males-1, females-2.

Measures of Variance

A misconception novices often have when calculating the mean is that the mean suffice to determine if statistical differences exist between means, e.g., preference for the iPhone compared with an android. What is important is the distance of each variable from that of the mean, also known as the *distribution*, to determine if statistical differences exist between two or more means. Worth noting is that distributions are not limited only to comparisons between means; they can apply to correlational analyses. (Correlational analyses are not discussed in this chapter. See suggested readings to learn more on this topic). The distribution of the variables from the mean informs about the reliability of the individual scores that comprise the sample. For example, a random sample taken from five individuals that were asked for their mobile phone preference; iPhone, the age ranged from 17, 21, 25, 27, and 30. From the five-age group data, the difference between the ages is large. But if the ages would be 17, 17, 18, 18, and 19, then the age difference between the values is small. The differences in distance (or distribution) of each individual age from that of the mean can be arrived at by calculating the *standard deviation* of each group. The standard deviation is an average of how far the individual scores are distributed (or distant) from the mean. Note that the variance is the standard deviation squared (Figure 4.3). When reporting statistical analyses, the standard deviation, rather than the variance, is commonly used to demonstrate the average distribution of the variables around the mean. A large standard deviation value signifies that the distribution of the individual samples varies greatly, i.e., some variables with small differences from the mean with other variables of large distances from the mean. A small standard deviation indicates that there is a small variation in the individual variables distribution from the mean. For example, if we wish to compare the significant differences of two means, the size of the standard deviation will determine the statistical difference and not the mean values (if two means of 50 and 25), it would appear that those two means can be statistically significant. A large standard deviation for both or one of the means is unlikely because there are statistical differences between the two means. For example, a large standard deviation of ten for the mean of 50 and standard deviation of five of the mean of 25, will yield a nonsignificant difference between the means because of the distribution of the means, 50 and 25, are two large. However, if the standard deviation is small for both means, statistical differences are most likely to exist between two means. The *range* is another measure of distribution in which this measure provides information about the spread of the variables by subtracting the largest variable from the smallest.

$$\text{Mean: } X = \frac{\sum X_i}{n}$$

$$\text{Variance: } S^2 = \frac{\sum X^2}{n-1}$$

$$\text{Standard Deviation: } S = \sqrt{\frac{\sum X^2}{n-1}}$$

$$\text{Standard Error of the mean: } SEM = \frac{S}{\sqrt{n}}$$

Figure 4.3

Group	Average	SD	SEM
iphone	20	3.15	0.58
Android	22	2.99	0.55

Figure 4.4

Standard deviation can be taken a step further to derive the *standard error of the mean* or SEM (Figure 4.3). The SEM is an estimate of how close the sample mean, $\bar{x}$, is to the real population mean, μ. If the SEM value is small, then the $\bar{x}$ is a good estimate of the μ. However, if the SEM is a large value, then the $\bar{x}$ is not a good estimate of the μ. Figure 4.5 illustrates the $\bar{x}$

estimating the μ by the size of the SEM size; the elliptical shape represents a population. The parameter μ represents the variable of interest of that population, for example, the average age of undergraduates that prefer iPhones. In the top figure, the bars that extend from the μ symbolize a small SEM signifying that the $\bar{x}$ lies within those bars and it is a good estimate of the μ. In contrast, the bottom figure, wherein the larger bars represent a large SEM, indicates that the $\bar{x}$ could fall anywhere within those large bars; therefore, it is a poor estimate of the μ.

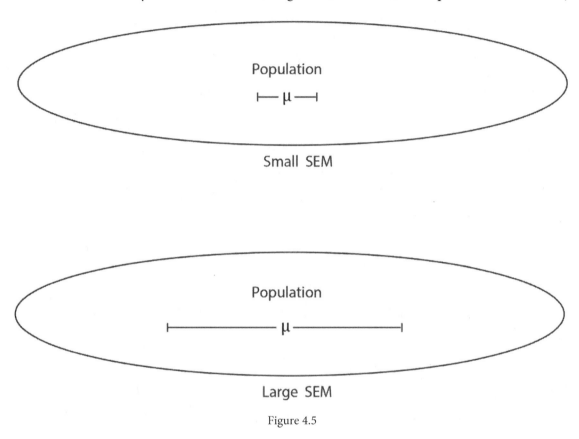

Figure 4.5

Misconceptions in Hypothesis Testing: The Meaning of "An Effect"

As mentioned in Chapter 1:, The Novel Researcher, a novice may have misconceptions of what an "effect" refers to. In the laboratory setting, "is there an effect," is lingo casually used when discussing statistical outcomes. The explanation of what is an "effect" is often understood to infer that the probability (or p-value) of equal or less than .05 confirms a hypothesis or "proves the hypothesis"; this understanding is a grave misconception. To appropriately apply statistics in hypothesis testing, see the following sections that provide explanations with examples.

Stating the Hypothesis

Statistics is a tool to test a hypothesis, therefore, hypotheses are formulated into statements from *research questions*. Hypotheses are biased because they state predictions. For example, the Apple research team's hypothesis, "Excel University undergraduates between the ages of 17 and 28 prefer the iPhone to an Android," is biased toward the preference for an iPhone. If a research team from Samsung's Android developers is interested in the same research question, then their hypothesis would be stated: Excel University undergraduates between the ages of 17 and 28 prefer an Android to the iPhones. According to the prediction stated, the expected outcome dictates the wording of the hypothesis statement.

Null Hypothesis and Alternative Hypothesis

Although the research team has an explicit bias toward what they believe the outcome will be, before running analyses the team must first word their hypothesis in such a way that it does not infer bias. Removing bias from the hypothesis statement is known as the *null hypothesis* (Ho). Null, meaning zero, infers that "there are no differences." Statistics test the null hypothesis based on the fundamental premise that hypotheses must be "disproved" and not the other way around (see Chapter 2: Defining Science chapter). The hypothesis with the explicit bias refers to the *research hypothesis* (Ha) or *alternative hypothesis* (Ha). Similar to the orange shirt analogy, samples are used to make inferences about populations and those inferences are based on probability. Most appropriately making a decision about the Ho is either to reject the Ho or fail to reject the Ho. Why does making decisions about the Ho in such a manner matter? It matters because regardless of how small the probability of an event not occurring is, the probability will never be zero; therefore, the research hypothesis can never be 100% ascertained or proven.

Examples of the (Ho) and (Ha)

Ho: Excel University undergraduates between the ages of 17 and 28 have no preference between iPhone and Android phones.

Ha: Excel University undergraduates between the ages of 17 and 28 have a preference between iPhone and Android phones.

Level of Significance and Rejecting the Ho

In making the correct decision to reject the Ho, a *level of significance* must be established based on probability. This level of significance is commonly at a probability of 5% (or .05). For example, if the decision is to reject the Ho from the example above, the decision claims that *the probability that undergraduates' preference of iPhones to Androids is so small (i.e., equal to or less than 5%), that the probability that students prefer iPhones to Androids is not attributable to chance.* Then it can be concluded that Excel University undergraduates between the ages of 17 and 28 *do* prefer iPhones to Androids. Hence, if rejecting the Ho was the correct decision, then the chances are higher in encountering an Excel University undergraduate between the age of 17 and 28 with an iPhone.

Failure to Reject the Ho

What happens if the probability is higher than .05? At this point, the decision is to fail to reject the Ho, which is interpreted as Excel University undergraduates between the ages of 17 and 28 who *do not* prefer iPhones to Androids. Therefore, if one were walking around the Excel

University campus, the chances of encountering an undergraduate between the age of 17 to 28 using an iPhone or Android are about the same. It is emphasized that statistics are a tool to make the decision of "rejecting" or "failing to reject" the Ho.

Type I Error

Recall that testing a sample is to identify if that sample represents the larger population. A Type I error is committed when the decision was to reject the Ho, i.e. "there were differences;" however, the decision should have been to fail to reject the Ho, i.e., "there were no differences." When a Type I error is committed, the inference between the sample and the population is misleading. From the example hypothesis, "undergraduates between the ages of 17 and 28 prefer iPhones to Androids," if the output of the analyses turned out to be less than a probability of .05, then the Ho is rejected. However, if the population of Excel University undergraduates between the ages of 17 and 28 have no preference for iPhones, a Type I error was committed. If Apple's research team believes that there is a preference for iPhones when there is not (Type I error), the company may conclude that they are dominating the market in a specific demographic. Consequently the company may lose out on investing in advertising or marketing strategies to increase their sales in that particular sociodemographic. More importantly, in research making a Type I error provides inaccurate research findings, and if these fiindings are published, not only are other researchers misguided by the findings, but so is society at-large.

Type II Error

If the research team's analyses from the sample data indicate that there is no preference between iPhone and Androids (a probability greater than 5%, or > .05), then the decision on the Ho is fail to reject. However, if the overall population of Excel University undergraduates between the ages of 17 and 28 does prefer iPhones to Androids, then a Type II error has been committed. In this situation, the Ho should be rejected, but the output of the analyses indicated otherwise. Consequently, Apple may invest on advertising and marketing that may not be necessary because this group of students already prefers iPhones.

Choosing the Probability Threshold

The level of significance is not set in stone. How is the level of significance determined? Selecting the probability is not an arbitrary choice, but a choice that will impact the likelihood of committing a Type I or Type II error. Some individuals prefer a smaller probability such as 1% (.01) or more flexible 10% (.10). The balance between Type I and II errors is similar to a seesaw; if the chances of committing a Type I error increases, then the chances of a Type II error decreases. Alternatively, if the chances of a Type I error decreases, the chances of a Type II error increases. These two scenarios rely on the probability (.01, .05, or .10) that was chosen to establish the level of significance to reject the Ho. For example, if the Apple research team chose a level of significance of 10 (10%), then the chances of committing a Type I error are higher. In context, if the team would repeat this experiment a couple more times, rejecting the Ho would occur more often (see Figure 4.6). There is more latitude to reject the Ho. However, if the company wants a stringent level of significance such as .01 (1%), there is a greater chance that the statistical output will be larger than .01; therefore, there is a higher chance of making the decision to fail to reject the Ho. This type of decision may increase the chance of committing a Type II error and conclude that there is no preference between iPhones and Androids phones. Would it be in Apple's best interest to set such a stringent level of significance? Probably not; only if they are highly confident that the sales are thriving in young college students and want to confirm this confidence for a particular sociodemographic would they set such a stringent level of significance. The Apple research team would want a probability that is not as high as 10% or low as 1%. Therefore, 5%, which is widely accepted, is adequate. Because scientific findings must be peer reviewed before findings can be published, setting a 10% probability can raise an eyebrow of concern about the reliability of the results if the Ho has a greater chance of being rejected. Peers may show more confidence in the findings if a more stringent level of confidence is set, i.e., 1%. However, most researchers would prefer not to set such stringent level of confidence because of the higher chance of failing to reject the Ho.

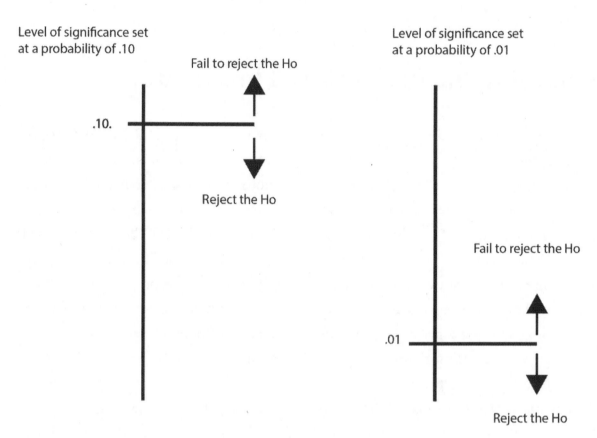

Figure 4.6

Statistical Interpretation

Most statistics books have tables in the appendix that provide information of *normalized data* used as a reference in making decisions about the Ho. These tables are the source for making decisions about the Ho. To correctly use the information contained in the tables, a few pieces of information are necessary: 1) *sample size*, 2) *degrees of freedom*, and 3) *level of significance*. These three pieces of information are linked to a *critical value*. The critical value is then compared with a *calculated value* (calculated value is derived from the sample data), and if the calculated value is greater than the critical value (Cal > Crit), then the decision is to reject the Ho. If the calculated value is smaller than the critical value (Cal < Crit), then the decision is to fail to reject the Ho.

With the availability of statistical software, a probability is calculated as part of the output, so there is no need to use the normalized data tables. For example, before the advent of statistical software, researchers would indicate a level of significance set at p < .05 marked with asterisks (*) to indicate the Ho was rejected. Today, with the use of statistical software, the output will show the exact level of significance; for example, p = .003. It is clear that a small probability of .003 is much smaller than a .05 and the decision of rejecting the Ho is with a high level of confidence.

When the Ho is true, and it is statistically rejected that is said to be the *power of the statistic* (β-1). For the power range between 0 and 100, the higher the value the stronger the *statistical power*. It is an indicator of how much confidence can be placed on the statistical output when the Ho is rejected. A power of 80% is considered a strong statistical analysis in rejecting the Ho.

Illustration of Distributions

Decisions of rejecting or failing to reject the Ho can be illustrated with bell-shaped curves that depict the center and distribution of sample data. Below are two bell-shaped area curves that hypothetically represent the variable of age and its distribution for two groups: those that prefer iPhones or those that prefer Androids. The overlap, or lack thereof, between two distributions can illustrate when the decision should be to reject or to fail to reject the Ho. If the bell-shape curves overlap, the decision is to fail to reject the Ho. The degree of overlap (hatched grayed area) signifies the strength of how different the two distributions are from each other (Figure 4.7, top). A little overlap means the two distributions are more different from each other, and a huge overlap means the two distributions are very similar to each other. In the illustration, the degree of overlap between the two curves (hatched gray area) suggests that age is not a factor in the preference of iPhone to Android phones. Because age is not a factor, it can be inferred that in regard to age both groups are from the same population or are one population. In contrast, the bottom bell-shape curves illustrate no overlap between the two distributions.

The non-overlapping distributions signify that the distributions for the variable, i.e., age, differs in preference for iPhone over Android phones (Figure 4.7, bottom), inferring that the variable age is a factor for phone-type preference. If age does differ in phone type, then the two distributions are from two different populations. As described in the previous section, when the Ho is rejected, this decision is interpreted as the age mean of those that prefer iPhones or android phones was was significantly different. The non-overlapping bell-shaped curves are an illustration of when the Ho is rejected and when the bell-shape curves do overlap significantly, which implies that the decision is a failure to reject the Ho.

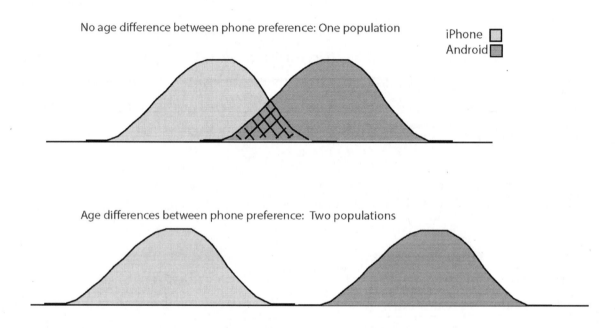

Figure 4.7

Graphical Representation of Statistics

Statistical outputs can be illustrated using graphs. Graphs must be organized and simplified to represent the data adequately. There are different types of graphs that include *histograms, bar* *graphs*, *line graphs*, *pie charts*, *scatterplots*, and *boxplots*. Bar graphs are the most common when comparing two or more means. Shown below is a bar graph showing two means for age from the sample data that represents undergraduates' preference for iPhone compared with Androids. To indicate if the level of significance is statistically significant, an asterisk (*) is placed above the error bars. The error bars are usually the SEM. The sample bar graphs shown below demonstrate two forms of indicating statistical significance when comparing two or three groups.

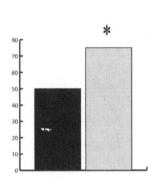
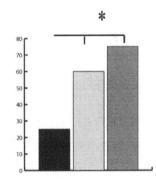

Figure 4.8

Graph Labels and *y*-Axis Variable Range

The sample data set includes an age range of 17 to 28. It would be meaningless to have a range of 0 to 100 years old *y*-axis variable. The bars would be too small to appreciate the mean comparisons. The sample graph has a *y*-axis variable range for ages starting at 16 and topping at 28. In the *x*-axis are the independent variables for phone type. The bars may be labeled appropriately, e.g., iPhone and Android, below the *x*-axis bar. Alternatively, a legend can be included as shown on the sample graph. The small bars extending both up and down (positive and negative) from the top of the bar (mean) indicate the SEMs. Note that no asterisks are shown above either bar, which signifies no statistical significances between the two means.

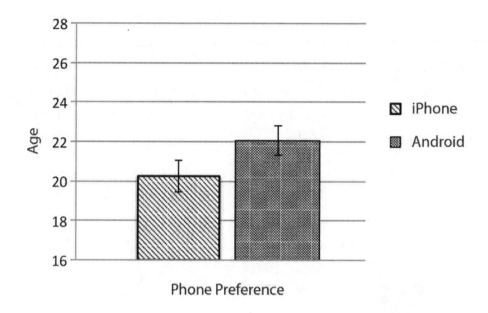

Figure 4.9

Interpretation of a Sample Statistic: Independent t-Test

A sample *t-test* statistic is shown below to demonstrate when two means are statistically different from each other. An *independent* t-test is a suitable statistic to use in this example because there are only two means to compare, and the mean from each group is independent from the other mean. That is, an individual of a certain age will either prefer iPhone or Androids. That individual's age cannot be in both groups. Therefore, the age mean of those that prefer iPhone is independent of the age mean that prefers Androids. A t-test, as well as all statistics, must meet certain assumptions. The topics on assumptions are outside the scope of this chapter. Consult a basic statistics book for topics of normally distributed data as well as parametric and nonparametric tests. Formulas are easy to find from statistical books and scholarly websites. The t-test statistics presented are only examples and not derived from actual data. Electronic spreadsheets such as Excel are available that are used to perform basic statistical tests. The example output of a t-test shown below (Figure 4.10) shows the following information: the variables (iPhone and Android groups), the number of variables (ages) per group, the sample mean (of age), and the sample standard deviation (of age). Below are two choices: two-tailed and one-tailed. If the researchers only care if age differences exist between the two groups, the t-test level of significance applies to a two-tailed test. If the researchers do care whether age is higher or lower for one group over the other in phone preference, then the level of significance applies to a one-tailed test.

The statistical analyses can be determined by two methods: First, the old-fashioned way, comparing the calculated value (1.61) with that of the critical value (2.05). The calculated value of 1.61 is not greater than the critical value of 2.05; therefore, the decision is fail to reject the Ho. Second is the modern approach. Because the output calculated a statistical p-value (.12) output, a decision can be made based on that probability. The statistical p-value is .12, which is much greater than .05; again, the decision is fail to reject the Ho. Either using the critical or calculated values or the statistical p-value, the conclusion should be the same—i.e., fail to reject. The interpretation of the decision is that there are no age differences between the Excel University undergraduates between the ages of 17 and 28 in their preference for iPhone or Android phones.

Compare Means: Independent T-test

VARIABLES	Sample size	Mean	Standard Deviation
iPhone	15	20.27	3.15
Android	15	22.07	2.99

t-test assuming unequal variances (heteroscedastic)
Degrees of Freedom 28
Hypothesized Mean Difference   0
Pooled Variance   9.42
Test Statistic 1.61

Two-tailed distribution
p-value   0.12   Critical Value (5%)   2.05

One-tailed distribution
Alternative hypothesis Ha: Mu ? Mu0 - Less than (lower-tailed)
p-value   0.06   Critical Value (5%)   1.70

Figure 4.10

Outliers and Statistical Outcomes

In the sample dataset, there appears to be a value in the iPhone group that may be an outlier—the age of 28. Outliers can influence the outcome of statistical analyses; therefore, it is good practice to always scan the data before running analyses to identify any outliers by graphing a box plot to quickly identify outliers. Otherwise, outliers may be determined by calculating the median, i.e., quartiles (Q1, Q3) and the interquartile range (IQR; Q3–Q1). Using the sample data for each group (Figure 4.2) the calculations are shown below to identify outliers.

The median for iPhone: the total sample size is 15; 15 /2 = 7.5. Counting from the lowest to highest, the number that sits in the position 7.5 is 19. Sometimes the median is not an odd number; in this case, the two values that sit in the middle position are added together then subtracted by two to obtain the median. Quartile 1 is calculated similarly to the median except with the values below the median. Count how many values sit below the median starting the counting from the median number. The number of variables that fall below the median are seven; to determine the value that represents Q1, find the position of that value by dividing seven into 2, i.e 7/2 = 3.5. The value that is in the 3.5 position sits between 18, 18. Add 18 + 18 then divide by 2 and that will equal 18, therefore Q1 is 18. Note that for this example the value that sits at the 3.5 position has the same value before and after it, i.e. 18; therefore, Q1 can easily be determined without the adding and division becuase the value would be the same, i.e. 18. The same is done for Q3: 7 samples, 7/2 = 3.5. The value that sits in the 3.5 position is 21; therefore, Q3 is 21. The interquartile range (Q3–Q1) is 21 – 18 = 3. Subtracting 18 (Q1) from 3 (IQR) yields the lower-end boundary, 15. Any sample value that falls below 15 is an outlier. Adding 21 (Q3) to 3 (IQR) yields a value of 24. Any value above 24 is an outlier. Therefore, for the iPhone dataset, 28 is an outlier. The same calculations can be performed for the Android group.

iPhone group: Median: 19; Q1: 18; Q3: 21; IQR: 3; lower boundary: 15, and upper boundary 24. Because 24 marks the highest value that is not an outlier, any value higher than 24 is an outlier.

Android group: Median 22; Q1: 19; Q3: 25; IQR: 6; lower boundary: 13, upper boundary 31. The values 13 and 31, respectively, are the lowest and highest values that mark the boundary for an outlier.

If outliers are identified, are they automatically removed from the analyses? Not exactly! If a value happens to be outside the lower or upper boundary, the data must be evaluated to verify that no errors occurred when recording the data or during data entry into a spreadsheet. If no mistakes were made when entering the data, then the information that pertains to that value must be scrutinized. If no extraneous circumstances are evident from the data collection to explain the outlier, then that data point should not be excluded from the dataset. Keep in mind that outliers can influence the statistical outcome of results. However, without documentation that validates why a value must be removed, the outcome must be accepted regardless of the influence the outlier has on the statistical outcome. For example, removing the value of 28 from the iPhone sample set would change the statistical outcome to rejecting the Ho. However, the criteria included the ages 17 to 28; therefore, without any additional information of that data point, it is appropriate to leave in that data point.

Refresher

Statistics is a tool to obtain information of a population from a sample. Measures of centrality and distributions are useful for determining statistical significance. The decisions that establish whether the sample is representative of the population are determined by setting a level of significance that is based on a probability to reject the Ho correctly. The level of significance will influence the degree of committing a Type I or II error. Illustrations of bell-shape curves that represent distributions of different populations are also useful in making a decision on the Ho depending on the degree of overlap between the distributions. Graphs are useful for simplifying statistical results and help illustrate what is significant with an asterisk (*) symbol. Outliers can influence means that can affect the decision of whether to reject or fail to reject the Ho. Data must be carefully examined before removing any data point to maintain the integrity of the data collection and statistical outcomes.

End-of-Chapter Exercises: Applying Concepts

1. Drake has decided to set a significance level of 5%, i.e., $p = .05$. His statistical analyses output indicates a p-value of 0.07. What decision should Drake make?

A. Fail to reject the alternative hypothesis.

B. Reject the null hypothesis.

C. Reject the alternative hypothesis.

D. Fail to reject the null hypothesis.

2. A Type II error is best expressed in

A. the significance level was set at a p-value of 0.05. The statistical analysis output was a p-value of 0.15. The decision was to fail to reject the Ho.

B. the significance level was set at a p-value of 0.05. The statistical analyses output was a p-value of 0.03. The decision was to reject the Ho.

C. the significance level was set at a p-value of 0.05. The statistical analysis output was a p-value of 0.03. The decision was fail to reject the Ho.

D. the significance level was set at a p-value of 0.05. The statistical analysis output was a p-value of 0.03. The decision was to reject the Ho.

3. If you set a significance level of 0.05, that is the probability you are willing to accept that

A. you are 5% right about rejecting the Ho.

B. you are 5% wrong about failing to reject the Ho.

C. you are 5% right about failing to reject the Ho.

D. you are 5% wrong about accepting the Ha.

E. you are 5% wrong about rejecting the Ho.

References

Gushanas, T. (Ed.). (2017). Twins study: About. Retrieved from https://www.nasa.gov/twins-study/about

U.S. and World Population Clock. (2017). Retrieved from https://www.census.gov/popclock/

Chapter 5: Scientific Literature

"To get to know, to discover, to publish – this is the destiny of a scientist."

–François Arago

Learning Objectives:

1. Explain the benefits of scientific literature.
2. Distinguish between the three different literature sources.
3. Identify the sections of an original and review the article.

Who is the targeted audience for primary and secondary literature compared with tertiary literature?

Significance of Scientific Literature

Science steers the direction of how individuals perceive the world and think about phenomenon. History has shown that without a written document of discovered phenomena, no matter what the discovery may be, that knowledge will not carry over to the next generations. Why does it matter if new discoveries are not passed on to future generations? The significance of science not disseminating throughout the generations is multifold: 1) people can end up trying to address a problem that has already been solved, i.e., the problem of "reinventing the wheel," 2) there is a loss of time, and 3) economical resources are consumed. However, the latter points are substantial; the significance of scientific literature can be best referenced to a historical event in which the scientific writings of Galileo Galilei were forbidden to be shared with the public because the writings strongly supported evidence against the geocentric view. Although Galileo's writings were leaked and eventually conceded, the act of forbidding Galileo's work or that of any scientist speaks volumes about the power of scientific documentation, i.e., scientific literature.

Scientific literature can be in written form or communicated orally, and once disseminated it becomes an archival record. It is a record that documents findings that are original and that can be replicated by others. Scientific literature helps determine what is not known and helps identify gaps in the literature that pave the path in developing new ideas or asking new questions. The significance of scientific literature is that it provides documentation of the *methodology* used and is an instrument for replicating the results.

Types of Scientific Literature

Primary Literature

Primary literature is written documentation that reports new findings that have not been published previously. One key characteristic of primary literature is that it provides *depth* of a scientific area. Primary literature is written with certain technicality so that it does not appeal to readers without scientific training. The terminology can be technical and associated to a specific research area. Primary literature consists of original findings that are written by the researcher who conducted the studies. The information includes experimental data and results and gives new research directions. Sources that are considered primary literature are referred to as original articles that are published in scientific journals.

Secondary Literature

Secondary literature is a collection of original sources that help synthesize existing information in the scientific literature on a specific topic. The form of communication is usually technical and is geared to an academic audience. Secondary sources integrate results of several original sources into one paper. In contrast to original literature, secondary literature offers breadth of a scientific area. Books and review articles are secondary literature. Books and review articles are sources that share copyrighted data from other sources. Secondary sources are useful when learning about a new scientific topic.

Tertiary Literature

Tertiary sources, unlike primary and secondary, are written in layman's terms, and technical terminology is usually defined within the text. Types of tertiary sources include news reports, briefings, and Wikipedia. Because the information found on Wikipedia can be modified by anyone and is often incomplete or incorrect, instructors dissuade students from doing research reports using Wikipedia as their literature source. The pamphlets found in doctors' offices are tertiary sources as well as the encyclopedia sets that were sold door to door by salespersons; however, now encyclopedias are not as common in households and are easily accessible through the Internet. Encyclopedias contain facts on almost any topic and can be used as a literature source for research reports.

Forms of Communicating Scientific Literature

Scientific information can be disseminated via a number of forms of communication *Electronic journals* are journals available directly from the journal's website. Most journals require a subscription fee to access the articles. Academic institutions subscribe to a number of journals that are accessible to the students, faculty, and staff. Also, articles that are not found in one institution can be accessed from another institution, whereby journals that are not subscribed to by one institution can be obtained through another associated institution that does pay subscription fees. Academic institutions have websites set up through their libraries that allow for easy access to journal articles. Access to electronic journals is available to the public but will require a one-time purchase of the scientific article of interest.

Google Scholar is a search engine useful for finding scientific sources. Google Scholar does not require an account setup and is free of charge. Searching for articles can be easy by using keywords to help search for a topic. For example, searching for articles on "diabetes in the elderly" would be more effective if three or four words were used to help narrow the search; words like aging, diabetes type 2, and elderly will have fewer articles to peruse through if only a few keywords were used.

Reports are considered scientific literature as long as the content of the reports was obtained by following the scientific method. These reports are usually prepared for grant-funded agencies such as the National Institutes of Health. Thesis reports inform of the strategies and progress of scientific inquiry. *Theses* are manuscripts that are written to demonstrate comprehension and mastery of a specific research topic. A committee composed of three to five members that have expertise in the area of research that the thesis is focused on, and a member that is not associated with the research, help guide the trainee in the process of writing the thesis. Once they have been presented with a written document of the thesis followed by an oral presentation, they approve or reject the thesis that was submitted to obtain a master's or Ph.D. degree. The thesis must be original material generated by the trainee. The completion of the thesis is traditionally the last stage in finishing graduate school. Undergraduates that are in honors programs also write theses; however, undergraduates' theses are closely monitored by the advisors and are much shorter in comparison to a master's or Ph.D. thesis. However, an honors thesis should also be original work. The goal for either an undergraduate or graduate (master's or Ph.D.) should be to publish his or her thesis work.

Posters are a means of communicating works in progress at scientific conferences. Scientific conferences are meetings that scientists attend to showcase their works in progress. The research presented must not be published, but rather sufficient findings to translate the objectives of the research. This type of research communication is presented on a piece of board paper that is organized into different sections: introduction, methods, results, and conclusions. It usually contains figures and graphs that help explain the ongoing research. It is a means of conveying information about ongoing projects and to receive feedback on that research.

Personal communications are a type of transfer of scholarly information between two experts that is orally communicated. This type of communication can be cited on manuscripts but is not used very often. It is most accepted when both sources are highly regarded and respected in the scientific community. Personal communication can include an expert take on a particular subject matter that may be under investigation.

Government documents are those most likely to be generated by the military engaged in research projects. These documents may be classified and only high officials have access to them. Over the years, some of these documents can become declassified and accessible to the public.

Verb Tense of Each Section of an Original Article

The language of each section of the manuscript guides the reader through the storytelling such as what happened in the past, what is happening in the present, and what to expect in the future. Scientific literature points to the authors' thinking process throughout the storytelling. Though scientific literature tends to be personalized with wording such as "our research," "we propose," or "our findings," it should avoid a first-, second-, or third- person narrative. It is best to state, "the research," "the proposed," or "the findings." Each section has its own tone created by the verb tense.

An introduction can vary in verb tense. Past research can be stated in the past if the work is no longer believed to be true, e.g., "falling objects were believed to fall faster according to weight." However, if citing previous research that is still supported and believed to be true, then the present tense is appropriate, e.g., "since the times of Galileo, it has been shown that falling objects fall relatively at the same rate." When describing another's methodology, past tense should be used, e.g., "Galileo tested his theory of falling objects using various objects of differing weights being dropped from different heights." The tense of the introduction should describe what information is no longer believed to be true and which information is still supported by research. Because the methods refer to research that already occurred, this section is written in the past tense. Because the results are reports of findings that already occurred, this section is written in the past tense, e.g., "adrenaline levels were higher in runners that reported to run one or more marathons per year." The discussion will have varying tenses that interpret what was found as well as the future direction of the research. The discussion can start with past tense, e.g., "the overall findings demonstrated that adrenaline can be increased with an intense running routine" or a present tense, e.g., "the overall findings show that adrenaline is increased with an intense running routine." The abstract, because it provides information of each section of the paper, should reflect the tense that is consistent with the section it describes.

Structure

Scientific literature is similar to other literature in that it tells a story. It has a beginning, a middle, and an end. The beginning includes an introduction that informs about what is already known about a certain topic and leads the reader to why there is an interest in a particular research topic. The middle informs of how the research is conducted and its outcome. The end provides a discussion that helps explain the outcomes of the study. The end also includes new directions in which the research can be steered. This section focuses on primary and secondary literature, specifically an original and a review article, respectively.

Title Page

The title page for an original and a review article are very similar. The title page provides information that helps the reader determine if the article is of relevance to the research interest. The title of an original article is technical with a narrow focus. In contrast, a review article's title is not as technical nor as specific. It describes the broader implications of a topic. A tertiary literature title is in layman's terms that are "newsy" and grasp the of readers' attention. Tertiary literature informs of scientific information but avoids technical terms.

The structure of the title page helps readers determine if the article is of relevance to their interests.

The title page informs which journal the article was published in. The article can easily be traced to the journal by the issue, date, year, and page number provided at the top of the title page, which proceeds the journal name. The authors are listed under the title page as well as the institutions or affiliations of each author. The institution may be a university or government agency.

The abstract, which is a summary of the entire paper, is on the title page. It is usually 300 to 500 words that provide the highlight of the paper. Information provided in an abstract helps the reader decide if the article is of relevance to his or her research topic.

Primary Literature—An Original Article

Abstract

The abstract is a synopsis of the entire article. It has a specific structure that starts with background about the topic of the paper. This first piece of information provides a broad introduction to the topic. The broader idea of the article is normally one sentence long. The following one or two sentences state what is not known or the problem that inspired the research reported in the article. A hypothesis statement or the purpose of the research is stated in one sentence. The methods are described in two or three sentences. There should be enough detail so that the reader can understand how the experiments were carried out. The results follow the methods. The results are the findings of the experiments and can be described in two or three sentences; however, only the key findings should be included in the abstract. A concluding statement can be one or two sentences that interpret the results and provide a future direction of the research (Table 5.1). The length of the abstract is determined by the requirements of the journal that the manuscript will be submitted to. Most of the content of the abstract is focused on the methods and results when amplitude is allowed, i.e., lengthier abstracts. A rule of thumb to follow is that the reader should be able to answer the following questions after reading an abstract: What is the broader topic? Why was the research important? Did the authors find an answer to the question(s) they were asking? What is key about those findings, and how is it relevant to future research? In answering these questions, the reader can decide whether the article relates to the research topic. The abstract follows the same organization of the sections of article.

Table 5.1: Original Article Abstract Format

Information	Recommended Length
Broader topic	1 sentence
Not known or problem	1 – 2 sentences
Hypothesis or purpose of the research	1 sentence
Methods	2 – 3 sentences
Results (key findings)	2 – 3 sentences
Conclusion	1 – 2 sentences

Introduction

The organization of the introduction can be thought of as an upside-down triangle that leads the reader from broader to specific topics (Figure 5.1). The first paragraph of the introduction informs about the broader area of the topic and the first sentence is normally a very general statement that captures the readers' interest. This first statement can include a statistic, such as "in the United States 300,000 cases of 'X' infections have been reported according to CDC 2017 reports." This type of opening statement lets the reader know the significance and focus of the literature (300,000 cases of "X" infections) and a frame of reference (in the United States). The following two paragraphs focus on what is known about the topic and in some cases is outlined in a chronological order. Summarizing what is already known requires that the writers select the information that is most pertinent to the research. Review articles are normally cited to help obtain an understanding of the research area. The couple of paragraphs that follow highlight the gaps that are present in literature or questions that have not been addressed. This section of the introduction sets the stage for introducing the thesis or hypothesis of the research. The last paragraph makes an argument as to why the research was important to conduct and completes the introduction with the last sentence stating the proposed research or hypothesis.

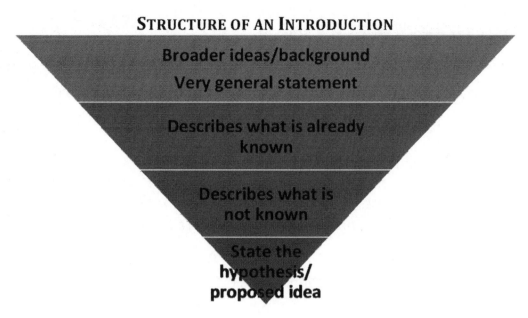

STRUCTURE OF AN INTRODUCTION

Information	Recommended Length
Broader Ideas/background	1st section, one paragraph, 1st sentence
Describes what is already known	2nd section, one or two paragraphs
Describes what is not known	3rd section, one or two paragraphs
States the hypothesis / proposed idea	Last section, last sentence

Figure 5.1: The structure of an introduction.

Methods

The experimental design is divided into materials and procedures collectively referred to as the *methods* section. The materials include all of the supplies that are used for carrying out the experiment and can include apparatuses and special equipment. This section informs whether the subjects are human or whether a model (and which type of model) was used. It states how many subjects were included in the study and outlines any inclusion and exclusion criteria. These criteria establish which subjects made the cohort of the study to strengthen the validity of the results. The procedures explain how the materials were used, the timeline of the study, how long the experiments took, and how many time points were included. Also described in this section is where the study was conducted, and also the compliance with both human or animal subjects' policies and regulations (e.g., IRB or IACUC protocols; see Chapter 6: Ethics in Research). The last part of the methods section describes the type of analyses or statistics that were used as well as the type of statistical software that was used for the data analyses, such as the Statistical Package for the Social Sciences or SPSS. In the methods section, illustrations can be included to help depict materials used for the experimentation.

Results

The results section follows. The results are the outcomes of the experiments, are very objective, and do not attempt to interpret the results. This section describes the results in the context of statistical analyses. The statistical analyses can also be presented in the form of tables or graphs. Illustrations of the results may also be included.

Discussion

The discussion interprets the results in the context of the existing literature. Specifically, an explanation is given of what the results mean. If the hypothesis is supported, then an explanation should be provided of how this new information fills in a gap that exists in the literature. The findings may not support a hypothesis, and in these circumstances the literature needs to be searched for information that may support the unexpected findings. In cases where a breakthrough in science has been achieved, there may be limited existing literature to support that finding. These types of breakthroughs set the tone for future experimentations that will be based on this finding. The length of the discussion may depend on how many findings came out of the experimentation. Also, the length of the discussion section depends on the journal's criteria for submission. The results need to be explained; what do the results mean? First, address if the hypothesis was supported or not. If it was supported, then from what is already known in the discussion, the results are interpreted as "data suggest" or "demonstrates."

Though it is more common to suggest future directions toward the end of the discussion, which can be the last one or two paragraphs, if there are several key findings, new directions can be stated when discussing each of the findings. The purpose of the discussion is to conceptualize in a theoretical manner the significance of the findings. Also, new data is not presented in the discussion section.

Review Article

The structure of a review article is different from that of an original article; however, it does follow the storytelling format with a beginning (introduction), middle (body), and end (conclusion). Some reviews will have an abstract included in the title page.

Abstract

Some review articles do not have abstracts. Similar to an original article the abstract is a summary of the entire article, but there are a few differences (Table 5.2). The background statement of a review, similar to an original article, states the broader ideas in one or two sentences. The broader statement informs the reader of the bigger picture of the topic, which is then followed by an introduction of the focus of the article. In one or two sentences, the reader should have an understanding of what the paper will cover. The key specifics of the review that will comprise the body of the article are mentioned in two or three sentences. This should include the purpose of the topic and more detail about what the paper will discuss. The last sentence should be a concluding remark that states the take home message of the review.

Table 5.2: Review Article Abstract Format

Information	Recommended Length
Broader topic	1 – 2 sentences
Introduction of paper	1 – 2 sentences
Body	1 – 3 sentences
Conclusion	1 sentence

Introduction

The introduction explains the motivation for the review. The authors provide an explanation of the purpose for the review starting with background information about the topic. The background will be broad and then focus on gaps or questions that remain unanswered in the literature.

Body (Subtopics; Synthesize Results from Other Sources)

The body of the review is the heart of the article and normally starts with an explanation of how the information was gathered to develop the review paper. For example, the author will mention that the literature sources were obtained from specific literature search engines, e.g., PubMed or Medline using specific keywords. Some reviews perform meta analyses of other literature sources to arrive at their own consensus of what is agreed upon or not agreed upon in regard to a certain topic. The methodology reported on a review, which is the means of how information was gathered or the approach that was taken to write the review, is different from the methods section in an original article. The body is organized with subheadings that help guide the reader's understanding of the topic. For example, a review on metabolic function of athletics is an overwhelming topic. The subheadings help introduce the topic in a logical progression of ideas; for example, the topics may be organized starting with cellular mechanism of metabolic function and progress to a broader topic such as physiological processes during athletic performance. The subheadings should follow a chronological order from most basic to most complex. Each subheading is a piece of the puzzle that together forms the bigger picture of the topic. Tables and figures can be included to help synthesize the information provided in the body.

Conclusion

The conclusion covers several points. First, it provides an overall summary of the literature, followed by a highlight of what gaps or questions exist in the literature. Then, a reasonable explanation of how a novel perspective from the author's point of view will fill in the gaps is presented, as well as new, proposed directions of future experimentation.

Acknowledgments

The information in the acknowledgments section is the same for both an original and a review article and gives credit to individuals and funding resources that supported the authors of an original or review manuscript. In this section, colleagues are recognized for helping read and edit the manuscript; however, they do not contribute to the ideas, experimentation, and writing of the manuscript. Also in this section, colleagues are recognized for providing gifts that helped make the research possible; for example, a colleague that synthesized a protein and provided that protein as a gift to the authors who performed the research. Lastly, funding sources such as government agencies or private donors are credited in this section. All funding sources have a numerical identifier that should be included next to the name of the funder. If different collaborators are contributing and are funded through different sources, each author's initials should be next to the funder's ID that funded that person.

Supplemental Information

Supplemental information is additional data that was not included in the manuscript but is pertinent to the overall story of the research project. These data may be pilot studies that helped shape the experiments from which the results are the focus. The supplemental data are tables and figures. These data are made in reference to the methods or results section. The guidelines provided by the journal will state the number of graphs or figures that can be included in the manuscript. Therefore, supplemental data can be included via a web link under the supplemental section of the manuscript.

Bibliography or References

This section lists all of the literature that is cited throughout the manuscript. The specific rules that explain how the citations should be listed depend on the citation source.

How to Read an Original or Review Article

The approach to reading scientific literature differs between an expert and a novice researcher. The expert already has a wealth of research background both in practice and reading that he or she focuses first on the methods and results. The expert can form his or her own interpretations with greater ease and can compare and find inconsistencies in the literature. As a result of a lack of knowledge, the novice will most often focus first on the introduction and skim through the methods and results. This is done primarily because the terminology is challenging, and the novice is unfamiliar with the methods and procedures described in the literature. Most novices read the discussion without challenging the author's work, and the results go unquestioned or challenged, again, as a result of the inexperience of the novice. The reader starts with a broader concept of the paper, and with each reading a more in-depth understanding develops. The reader decides which strategy helps best capture the key points of a research paper; however, a general guideline is provided in Table 5.3. A research paper usually requires more than one reading. The first reading helps familiarize the reader with the overall topic and ideas of the paper, and the second reading helps with understanding the finer points of the research. Most likely, it will require more than two times to read an article. The reader should jot down key points that the author makes to help extract the main ideas of the literature. Equally as important, the reader must jot down his or her own impressions and interpretations of the literature. To keep track, a sample table (Table 5.4) is provided to help organize the literature with the author's points as well as that of the reader's, i.e., your points. Jotting down questions, as recommended in Table 5.3, helps guide the reading, and if answers to the questions are found they can be jotted down under the reader's points. By recording all of the main ideas that the author cites as well as those of the reader, a clear distinction can be made of which ideas come from the author and which ideas come from the reader. This approach helps avoid plagiarizing and facilitates writing and researching papers because much of the initial jotting down of ideas occurred while the information was fresh, and was therefore jotted down in an organized manner.

Table 5.3 General Guidelines for Reading an Original or Review Article

Steps	
1	Read the abstract.
2	Read the bolded sections.
3	Read the article lightly.
4	While reading lightly, make a list of terminology and vocabulary that is unfamiliar.
5	Define each term written on the list.
6	Review the graphs and figures (if provided in a review).
7	Jot down questions after the light reading.
8	Read each section again, and answer the questions.
9	Note any conclusions of your own before reading the authors conclusions.
10	Compare your conclusions to that of the authors.

Table 5.4

Author	Journal	Year	Title	Questions
Bandura, Albert	Journal of Personality and Social Psychology	1977	Cognitive Processes Mediating Behavioral Change	What are psychological procedures? What is the common cognitive mechanism? How are efficacy expectations different from response-outcome expectancies? How was fear arousal measured? How is microanalysis of self-efficacy and behavioral change?

AUTHOR HIGHLIGHTS

- **Behavioral change altered through strength of perceived self-efficacy**
- Social learning analysis, there are 4 main sources of information that the expectations of personal efficacy are derived or stem from.
- **Performance accomplishments are the best source to provide information of efficacy because it shows experience of personal mastery.**
- **Vicarious experiences can allow observers that watch others succeed influence their perception's that they too can succeed.**
- **Verbal persuasion**
- **Emotional arousal**
- Study used different modes of treatments to determine the effectives of each treatment to predict self-efficacy
- **Efficacy expectations vary in dimensions.** Individuals' perception can be arranged from easy, moderate, or difficult as to what an individual will engage in and in turn affect performance.
- **Efficacy expectations range in generality.**
- **Efficacy expectations range in strength.**
- **This study was to**
    1. **measure the different power or influence of personally performing a task or vicariously observation of someone else performing a task**
    2. **to test if behavioral change is altered by perceived self-efficacy**

    Participants: snake phobics

Treatments: direct mastering experience, modeling only, no treatment

Measured: a) dimensionality, strength, generality of efficacy expectation, b) approach behavior and fear arousal

PREDICTIONS:

The direct mastering experience would produce more generality, stronger, and higher dimensions.

The level of self-efficacy would result in variations in attempts or performance between the treatments, within the same treatment and the level of difficulty of each specific task, i.e. placing hand in front of snake ranging from holding snake.

Behavioral avoidance task (performance capabilities): involved 29 behavioral tasks that increased in threatening interactions with a snake.

Fear arousal: rated from 1 to 10 the fear arousal subject felt for each snake approach task when the tasks were described and then again when they had to perform it themselves.

A **fear index** was derived by averaging all of the fear response ratings.

Efficacy expectations: Measured obtained after behavioral avoidance pretest. Separate measures were obtained of magnitude, strength, and generality of expectations.

Situational generalization of fear and self-efficacy: Used snakes that differed from the one used in the test.

READER POINTS

- Response-outcome refers to that a specific behavior will predict a particular outcome. However, efficacy refers to the conviction invested to successfully produce a certain behavior that will lead to desired outcome.
- Bandura is using individuals with pre-existing phobias to measure their self-efficacy through performance and vicarious treatments. Key here, students' perception of a task being difficult and un-accomplishable may not be clear what past experience may contribute a perception of unattainability. What are the triggers that will stimulate a sense of defeat before attempting a task or giving up mid-attempt? Does this matter? Through guidance of a particular task be sufficient to change behavioral perception and stimulate or strengthen a weak self-efficacy that leads to behavioral change, hence accomplishing the task. Will accomplishing the task initiate a change of behaviors that will stimulate future attempts and persistence to complete tasks, ergo further strengthening the sense of belief that can achieve the task at hand even though it is novel, challenging, and even threatening.

- What is key here is that this paradigm is based on overcoming a fear. Self-efficacy linked to fear as the roadblock to take action and complete a task.

Author	Journal	Year	Title	Questions
Bandura, Albert	Psychological Review	1977	Self-efficacy: Toward a Unifying Theory of Behavioral Change	What is meant by cognitive locus of operation?

AUTHOR HIGHLIGHTS

- Cognitive locus of operation implies that there is a location where cognitive processes take place.
- In setting up the theory the author states that it was originally believed that psychological treatments functioned through "peripheral mechanisms" resulting in automatic new behavior
- Also, reinforcement promoted new behaviors without any conscious awareness involvement
- The peripheral mechanism explanations of behavior were then replaced by theories of "central processing" that involved direct, vicarious, and symbolic source of information.

READER POINTS

- The titled implies the author proposes a theory that ties in concepts towards behavioral change.
- It is claimed that if an individual engages in a situation that is perceived to be threatening but it actually is safe, that individual will perceive the experience as one that they can cope with and this in turn will strengthen their self-efficacy. Such experience may cease their fear.
- However, if someone does not complete a behavior, then no impact will be made on strengthening their self-efficacy. Thereby continue to feel that he/she cannot carry out a specific behavior.
- Stating that a person will display defensive behavior towards a threat but mostly because the individual believes that based on past occurrences that the threat will produce some aversive consequence (i.e. pain). However, even though the threat will no longer produce an aversive consequence, the individual will continue to display defensive behavior due to the predictive value of the threat and not necessarily to the aversive consequence of the threat, such as the absence of pain.

Organizing Scientific Literature Ideas

The Peer Review Process

Manuscript Development

Before preparing a manuscript, the journal to which the article will be submitted must be decided upon. Each journal has its own specifications of a manuscript's format and length.

Primary and secondary sources normally go through a peer review process before it can be published. Tertiary sources are not required to go through the peer review process. This is one of the reasons instructors shy away students from using Wikipedia sources. Before starting to write a manuscript, a journal must be selected because each journal provides specific instructions to the authors on the format of the manuscript and, most importantly, the topics that journal is interested in publishing. Journals are rated by an impact factor that indicates how often that journal is cited. The list of journals and their impact factors are found in the *Journal Citation Reports*. A high impact factor alludes to fact that the journal publishes scientific works that may be on the cutting edge of science or reveal new technologies. However, many journals publish sound scientific findings that do not have high-impact factors.

It is important to keep in mind when submitting manuscripts for publication that manuscripts can only be submitted to one journal at a time for review. It may take weeks or months before the editor notifies the authors of the decision on their manuscript. It is unethical to try to submit the same manuscript to two or more journals in the hopes that if it is rejected by one journal another journal will accept the manuscript. The authors must wait to hear from the journal's editor before making a decision about whether to resubmit the manuscript to different journals.

Submit to Editor

When a manuscript is submitted for publication, the journal editor will review the article and determine if the manuscript will be peer reviewed by experts in the field or decide that the manuscript does not meet the journal's guidelines. If the manuscript was deemed not publishable by that journal, the editor will notify the authors that the manuscript will not be considered for publication in that specific journal. Once denied, the manuscript can then be submitted to another journal. If the editor finds that the manuscript has met the journal's guidelines and is of sound scientific quality, the editor will notify the authors that the manuscript was submitted for peer review. In most cases, three reviewers are asked to score the manuscript and provide the feedback that supports their score. In certain circumstances only two reviewers will review the manuscript. Once the reviewers submit their scores and comments and decide whether the manuscript should be published, the editor compiles that information and makes the final decision on the publication. In most cases, manuscripts will require some revisions before being accepted for publication. On the title page, two dates are shown: one date that indicates the initial submission and another date that indicates the acceptance for publication. In rare occasions, but a dream of all scientists, a manuscript will be accepted without any revisions; however, with two or three individuals reviewing a scientific work, there is always a point of argument and skepticism that challenges the author to have supporting evidence of the reported findings. It is expected that skepticism will play a role in the peer review process because that holds all scientists to the utmost ethical standards. Once the manuscript is accepted, the editor remits it to the authors for a final revision or proofs. Only grammatical corrections and minor revisions can be made on the proofs. Once the editor receives the proofs, the manuscript is submitted for publication. The published version is now referred to as an article. Nowadays, articles are published online ahead of the paper version to expedite the accessibility of the findings.

Citations

All publications are archived in the journal with the date, year, volume, issue, and number of pages to provide access to the article. The title page contains all of the archival information. In-text citations refer to making reference to an article from which the information was obtained.

When making reference to ideas that come from published or unpublished literature, they must be cited in the text where the information is mentioned.

Citation Formats

There are a number of citation formats that may cause confusion for the researcher if he or she is not familiar with which is the appropriate one to use. The best avenue for deciding which one to use is following the journal's instructions for publication. Citation formats may require using the author's last name and publication date when referencing a specific article in the text where it is mentioned. However, other formats will require numbering the citations and will not show the name of the author. There is a preference that a format includes the author's name rather than a number because it becomes cumbersome if the reader is required to flip to the bibliography page at the end of the article to find a particular citation listed in the text. Also, having the author and year of publication facilitates the storytelling of the article. Most research journals will require the American Psychological Association (APA) or Modern Language Association (MLA) format.

Electronic reference formats simplifies the work of having to type each citation in the text or in the reference or bibliographical list at the end of the article. The software programs most commonly used by researchers are EndNote, Mendeley, and RefWorks; however, there are several reference format programs that can be used with different computer operating systems. Electronic reference formats permit the writer to cite scientific works while developing a manuscript without being concerned with having to rewrite an entire paper when an additional reference is needed or the references are rearranged in the text. The reference list can easily be generated with one single push of a button that formats the references according to the selected citation format, e.g., APA. Using reference software also helps generate a library of references that can be referred to and used for other manuscripts. These reference libraries can be safely stored without the risk for losing information. This type of software has facilitated the writing of research documents that would otherwise be cumbersome and time consuming.

Scientific Literature Search Engines

The accessibility of the World Wide Web (WWW) has led to the development of search engines such as Google, Bing, and Yahoo. Out of habit, the novice resorts to Google as the first choice when searching academic sources. However, information from sites such as Wikipedia, which is not peer reviewed, is frowned upon. Wikipedia is the first source of information that people typically seek; however, when searching scientific literature, there are databases such as PubMed, Medline, or ScienceDirect that are specifically designed to search for scientific literature. Google has developed a scholarly search engine called Google Scholar. When performing a search for a specific topic using the scientific databases, using keywords can help narrow the number of articles that are available in the database. For example, if the topic of interest is social media, a PubMed search will display 15,831 articles that contain the words *social media*. The topic should to be narrowed down to obtain a smaller pool of specific articles. Entering keywords helps narrow the number of articles that turn up, for example keywords such as social media, undergraduates, learning, performance will result inthree articles which is significantly less compared with 15,831 articles when use only one keyword, social media. Normally, three to five keywords should suffice to narrow the topic significantly but obtain a good number of articles that are closely related to the topic. If a specific author's work is of interest, then the author's last name and first initial can be entered to retrieve a selected pool of articles that mention that author's name. Take caution that more than one author can have the same name and may also share the same research area. For example, a PubMed search for "Holguin, A." will prompt two scientists in the area of HIV; one of whom is from the United States and focuses on neurocognitive function, and the other who is from Spain and does work in molecular studies of HIV. Some knowledge about the author must be known before performing a literature search to retrieve the literature of the desired author. Search engines are free; however, the articles may not be free. Once the article of interest is selected, the search engine redirects to the website where the article is published. For scientific articles, the engine will redirect the search to the journal website that published the work. Some publications are free to download, i.e., *open-access articles*, or a fee is required to purchase the article. Colleges and universities can be linked within their school systems, providing access to library resources from one institution to another. The access to literature between institutions allows for a larger pool of sources. In situations where an article is not available because of the lack of subscription to the journal where it is published, the article can be ordered through *interlibrary services*.

Universities and colleges offer this service at no cost or a charge by the page. However, if access to a library is available, it is never a bad idea to visit the library and peruse the scholarly works.

Refresher

Science provokes inquiry about how individuals think of phenomena or become aware of phenomena. Scientific literature is a means of documenting scientific findings that form a bridge connecting the past with the present and the future direction of scientific findings. There are three main types of scientific writings: primary, secondary, and tertiary. Each of the three different types of scientific literature follows a specific structure. Primary literature provides depth and reports new findings, whereas secondary literature provides breadth and reports published data. Tertiary sources also report published data; however, this form of writing is geared toward the general public. Scientific literature can be transmitted in a number of forms such as electronic journals. The language or verb tense used in scientific writing depends on if it is primary, secondary, or tertiary. A title page contains the archival information and an abstract. An original article and a review article are structured differently in which the sections of an original article are composed of an introduction, methods, results, and discussion, whereas a review article is composed of an introduction, body, and discussion. All scientific writings include an acknowledgment and bibliography (or reference) section. In certain cases, supplemental data is accessible via a web link to support the findings on an article. Scientific literature goes through a peer review process to ensure that what is reported is sound science. Once a manuscript has been approved for publication, i.e., an article, then it can be retrieved using various search engines. When compiling information for primary, secondary, or tertiary literature, always to keep in mind that all scientific writing tells a story with a beginning, a middle, and an end.

End-of-Chapter Exercises: Applying Concepts

1. What are the differences between an original article, a review article, and a newsletter?
2. How is an original article organized compared with a review article?

3. What would happen if no record of scientific literature existed of Galileo Galilei's scientific arguments?

Chapter 6: Ethics in Research

"It seems paradoxical that scientific research, in many ways one of the most questioning and skeptical of human activities, should be dependent on personal trust. But the fact is that without trust the research enterprise could not function."

- Arnold S. Relman, *Editor, New England Journal of Medicine, 1983*

Learning Objectives:

1. Explain the role of trust in research.
2. Recognize unethical behavior in research.
3. Become familiar with the rules and regulations that uphold ethical behavior in research.

Which group of individuals are most susceptible to unethical treatment and why?

Trust

These days, scientists perform their work more often with teams and less often by themselves. The perception of a scientist is that of an individual wearing a white lab coat working busily in a laboratory that is filled with glassed flasks. That perception creates an impression that the scientist is up to something mischievous. Scientists rarely fit that description of the "lone scientists" but work with teams that comprise other colleagues, technicians, volunteers, and apprentices (graduate students). Yet, when reporting new findings, the findings are put under unwavering skepticism from the scientific community that questions the validity and reliability of the findings and can remain skeptical until someone else replicates the findings. This skepticism is necessary as checks and balance within the scientific community. Why is this skepticism so important in research? Simply because hypotheses are biased statements and although all experimentation must have an element of falsifiability (see Chapter 2: Defining Science), it is human nature for individuals to wish to confirm their hypotheses. Also, novel findings may have different interpretations, and the significance of how the results are interpreted will steer the following questions. Hence, skepticism and constructive criticism must be part of the peer review process for those that claim to have discovered a novel phenomenon. However, once probed from all angles, the scientific community must accept the findings if no evidence of misconduct was found while performing, collecting, and interpreting the data. Hence, trust must be part of research if science is to prevail. The best judge of scientific advancements is time because it will dictate which findings sustain replication. Trust between colleagues who work together on a daily basis, between colleagues that peer review each other's work, and between the scientific community with society at-large all come together to help protect the integrity of research.

The idea of trust in conducting research has always been an expectation that scientists are conducting themselves to the upmost ethical standards. History, though, reveals many instances where trust has not only been defied, but its consequences have rippling detrimental effects including affecting individuals (or animals) that are used as subjects in experimentation, abuse of monetary resources, misleading findings that cause much loss of time and effort replicating those findings, loss of respectable careers, and the loss of faith in science from society at-large.

What is considered unethical behavior? Unethical behavior lacks values, honesty, forthrightness, transparency, compassion, and fairness. Unethical behavior lacks accountability for negative consequences that the scientific findings may impose on any living organism (humans, animals, or vegetation) and nature (Earth or universe) for selfish gain, e.g., notoriety or monetary.

Illness-Free—Is It Ethical?

A new technology called CRISPER (clustered regularly interspaced short palindromic repeats)[1] has made it possible to modify genomes by slicing out specific genes, preventing the expression of those genes. CRISPER may have incredible promise for individuals with predispositions to cancer or other illnesses. Although the experimentation is in its early stages, scientists have removed targeted genes believed to express later in the organism that develop into disease[2]. With the excitement of new discoveries that make people healthier, there is great fear that such technology can lead to engineering humans. Scientists that are advancing this research argue that the objective is to remove genes that will awaken at some point during a lifetime and develop into a specific disease. Others argue that having the means to successfully alter genes by any means opens the door to modifying the human gene code, thereby creating engineered genes for humans. Interestingly, in the last few years, scientists have been creating new applications to the technology[3].

Scientists are tasked with abiding by a moral code while pushing forward for new advancements that can extend human life by trying to prevent genetically predisposed illnesses. Now it is well-recognized that the environment plays a strong role in the development of illnesses that can overrule a genetic predisposition. It is known that illnesses such as diabetes or hypertension, although inherited, are illnesses can be prevented through lifestyle changes.

Something to think about:

As a novel researcher, what is your stance on this subject?

Should scientists not pursue technological advancements if the long-term effects of such technology cannot be predicted?

What are the consequences for humans if an individual does not have to work toward staying healthy to prevent illness?

Who would have access to such technology?

Sources:

Horvath, P. and R. Barrangou. "CRISPR/Cas, the Immune System of Bacteria and Archaea." *Science*. January 2010. **http://science.sciencemag.org/content/327/5962/167.full**

Kaiser, J. "U.S. Panel Gives Yellow Light to Human Embryo Editing." *Science*. February 14, 2017.

http://www.sciencemag.org/news/2017/02/us-panel-gives-yellow-light-human-embryo-editing

Ledford, H. "CRISPR: Gene Editing is Just the Beginning: The Real Power of the Biological Tool Lies in Exploring how Genomes Work." *Nature*. March 7, 2016.

http://www.nature.com/news/crispr-gene-editing-is-just-the-beginning-1.19510

The abuse of trust with unchecked behavior has left a history of research with innumerable archives and research practices that violated the one cardinal rule, which is to protect the dignity and safety of the subjects that are involved in the research. History has recorded a number of research cases (Table 6.1) that have a resonating theme of vulnerable populations that have been taken advantage of, such as prisoners, minorities, orphans, and gays. Also, animals are a vulnerable population in research that has suffered abuse, unnecessary procedures, and neglect in certain cases. In the past, these populations were vulnerable because of the absence of regulations and policies to ensure their protection. The Tuskegee Experiment epitomizes the unaccountable human suffering and descent toward inhumanity over the course of several years (Table 6.1). The Belmont Report was created in response to the unscrupulous human conduct that took place during the Tuskegee Experiment and other studies found to be unethical. Ethical behavior guidelines must be complied with when human subjects or animals are part of research projects.

Unethical Research Practices	Period
Syphilis treatments	1876–1928
Testicular transplants experiments	1920
The Tuskegee Experiment	1932–1972
HeLa cells	1951
Milgram Experiment	1963
Tearoom Trade	1965–1968
Learned helplessness	1967
Pit of despair	1970
Stanford Prison Experiment	1971
Spring monkeys	1981–1991
Embryonic stem cell cloning	2006

Table 6.1: Cases of Unethical Research Conduct

The violation of human (or animal) rights in the unrelenting pursuit for self-validation compelled governmental agencies to implement rules, policies, and regulations to protect those who participate as subjects in research and hold accountable those who use unethical research practices.

The National Academy of Science, a nonprofit, private agency, was created by the United States Congress in 1863 to advise the federal government on all matters of scientific nature. With revelations of unbecoming behavior over the years, regulations, laws, and policies have been developed and enforced (Table 6.2).

Table 6.2: Laws, Policy, and Regulations

Milestone	Period
Food and Drug Act	1938
Nuremberg Code	1947
International Code of Medical Ethics of the World Medical Assembly	1949
NIH Medical Center Policy	1953
NIH Medical Board Document No. 1	1953
Kefauver-Harris amendments to the 1938 Food, Drug, and Cosmetic (FD&C) Act	1962
Federal Drug Administration regulations	1963
Helsinki Declaration	1964
U.S. Surgeon General policy statement	1966
National Research Act	1974
Regulations for the Protection of Human Subjects of Biomedical and Behavioral Research	1974
45 CFR 46 Subpart B	1974
Belmont Report	1979
President's Commission for the Study of Ethical Problems in Medicine and Biomedical and Behavioral Research	1980–1983
Common Federal Policy for the Protection of Human Subjects	1991
Final report of Advisory Committee on Human Radiation Experiments	1995
National Bioethics Advisory Commission	1995–2001
International Conference on Harmonization, Guidelines E6: Good Clinical Practice, Consolidation Guideline	1996
Animal Welfare Act	1996
World Health Organization Operational guidelines for ethics committees that review biomedical research	2000
Best Pharmaceuticals for Children Act	2001
Public Health Service Policy on Humane Care and Use of Laboratory Animals	2002

Human Research

The *Institutional Review Board* (*IRB*), which functions under the National Institute of Environmental Health Sciences (NIEHS), must review all human-subject research (https://www.niehs.nih.gov/about/boards/irb/index.cfm). The IRB mandate is to protect the welfare and well being of humans and ensure the compliance of governmental policies that include local, state, and federal, and those of the NIEHS and National Institute of Health. The IRB makes certain that all ethical standards are in compliance as outlined in the Belmont Report, which includes boundaries between practice and research, basic ethical principles, and applications. When a research project involves more than one institution, state, or country, IRB approval must be obtained from each institution that is participating in that research, and compliance with each institution's regulations must be adhered to. All institutions that participate in research have established regulations and policies that are accessible through their websites.

The Declaration of Helsinki was adopted in 1964 by the *World Medical Association* and amended over the years by the general assembly that is held around the world. The declaration outlines a series of ethical principles for biomedical research practices that involve both humans and animals. As stated in the declaration, "*The purpose of biomedical research involving human subjects must be to improve diagnostic, therapeutic and prophylactic procedures and the understanding of the etiology and pathogenesis of disease.*" This statement embraces the overall significance of the Declaration of Helsinki.

Consent

Research practices that are now regarded as unethical all had in common that they failed to notify the participants or subjects that either they were actually part of a study or held pertinent information that could impact their health. For example,n the Tearoom Trade (1965–1968) study where men having intimate relationships in public restrooms were being observed as part of an experiment without their knowledge . In The Tuskegee Experiment (1932–1972) they failed to advise participants of the risks of syphilis and withheldinformation that treatment had become available In the case of Henrietta Lacks, researchers developed cancer cell lines from a sick patient who was not informed her specimens were used for research (HeLa Cells 1951). All of these examples violated one of the principles of the Declaration of Helsinki, which states, "*Concern for the interests of the subject must always prevail over the interests of science and society.*" This statement must be given due process because any researcher must fully recognize that regardless of the significance the research can bring about, if the research imposes a hazard to the participant's well being and the risks outweigh the benefits, that research must not be carried out. When the risks are minimal and the benefits outweigh the risks, the participant must be informed in writing. Written consent must inform of the purpose of the research, what the participant's role will be in the research process, what potential risks he or she may encounter, any painful procedures that may be incurred, and what benefits he or she will receive from participating in the research. For example, a study that will test the efficacy of a drug will involve a subject in administering the drug and also providing specimens, such as blood, urine, or stool. If blood is required to be drawn, the participant must be informed, in writing, of the risk for having blood drawn, e.g., the potential for infection and the level of pain that the participant may experience from the needle prick. In a study that involves drug testing, the participant may be informed that he or she will receive medical attention throughout the study as well as monetary compensation. The participant also must be informed that the results obtained from his or her participation will form part of a larger database, that his or her personal information is confidential, and that at all times his or her contribution to the database will only be referenced with a numeral code and never by any identifier that reveals personal identity. All consents must provide these reassurances to the participants. The consent must also clearly inform that any participation is voluntary and that the participant holds the right to remove him- or herself from the study at any time. The participant must always feel free to exit the research project and should not be subjected to coercion or persuasion. Also, the participant must be informed that if the medical personnel or investigator feel that the participant's well being is at risk, he or she can stop the investigation at any time. The consent must have the names of the investigators that are responsible for the overall project and any collaborators that will be in direct contact with the participant. A valid consent form must have the participant's signature, otherwise it should be voided. When the participant is not of legal age, depending on the country where the research takes place, the parent or legal guardian can sign on his or her behalf.

Animal Regulations

Animals used in research have also been subjected to abuse and neglect (Table 6.1). The *Institutional Animal Care and Use Committee* (*IACUC*), instituted by the Animal Welfare Act, upholds any institution, government or private, to adhere to rules and regulations that protect animals from suffering and neglect according to the Public Health of Service Policy on Humane Care and Use of Laboratory Animals and the Guide for the Care and Use of Laboratory Animals (https://grants.nih.gov/grants/olaw/tutorial/iacuc.htm). No animal research may be conducted without the approval of the IACUC. This committee is responsible for reviewing the institutional protocols for the humane care and use of animals, inspection of animal facilities, preparing reports and making recommendations to the institutional official, reviewing concerns that involve the welfare of animals, reviewing and approving any activity that involves care and use of animals, and reviewing and approving changes that are necessary for ongoing activities with animals. The IACUC has the power to suspend any research using animals if any activity is in violation of the policies and guidelines.

Data

Researchers rely on data to interpret and make sense of the phenomena that are under investigation. How the data are handled will determine the direction of the new information. What is data? Data are the findings that are derived from experimentation. Data can be thought of as the output (or outcomes) after a series of steps have taken place in the planning and implementation of the experiment. The output must be respected regardless of if it supports a hypothesis or not. When unexpected outcomes are derived, the researcher's challenge is to interpret those results within the context of the available literature. What is the handling of data? The handling of data occurs at different levels during the experiment's design, during the collection of data, during the inclusion or exclusion of data points, and during the interpretation of the data.

Experimental Design

During the experiment's design, many decisions are made that can and will influence the outcome of the experiment. The principle of falsifiability (see Chapter 2: Defining Science and Chapter 4: Basic Statistics) should be embedded within the experiment's design. For example, if the experiment is designed to test whether men and women differ in phone-texting speed, then both genders must be exposed to the same conditions. What would happen if two different phones were used or if each gender was given a different passage to text? If this were to happen, then the output of the experiment would not accurately reflect a true comparison between the two groups. Also embedded in the experiment's design are criteria of reproducibility and empirical evidence. If these two criteria are not part of the design, the findings cannot be replicated. Thoughtful consideration to details is key to designing experiments.

Collection of Data

When collecting the data, much care should be taken to protect the integrity of the data and ensure that the output (results) are not influenced by carelessness, neglect, or manipulation. Using the example of comparing phone-texting speed between genders, the accuracy of the timing for each gender will determine the results. If the timer is started before the person starts to text or is left running after the person is finished texting, the integrity of that data has been compromised and no longer represents an accurate data point. When recording the texting speed on a spreadsheet, careful attention must be given to the accuracy of each data point. The data set must be scanned to verify no mistakes were made during the recording of the data. These days, most data are collected by sophisticated equipment that depends on the reliability and validity of said equipment. Periodic maintenance of all equipment used in scientific ventures must be done to ensure its proper functioning. Also, appropriate training in the use of any scientific equipment must be performed. Some equipment requires warming up before use or special solutions to ensure efficient operation. The careful management of equipment can help protect the integrity of the data that will be collected from such devices. Following data collection, the data may contain values that are potential mistakes in the data entry or are outliers. The decisions taken in leaving a data point or removing it can have a significant influence on the analyses' output. As described in Chapter 4: Basic Statistics, even if a value falls outside the range of the data set or outlier, that does not mean that the data point gets removed from the data set.

Inclusion or Exclusion of Data Points

A process of examining the experimental design and the circumstances of an outlier must be thorough before deciding to remove any data point. For instance, in the example of men versus women phone-texting speed, one of the entries is three times higher than all the other entries. A value that high would most likely be considered a mathematical outlier. If it happened to be the case that one of the participants had a very slow time speed attributable to just being slow at texting, then that data point should remain. However, if it happened that the individual suffers from some type of limitation with using his or her fingers, then removing that data point would be validated. This problem can be avoided before initiating the experiment by establishing inclusion and exclusion criteria; for instance, a person with any medical condition or impairment that might limit using the phone's texting feature would be excluded from participating. If any data point is removed, a notation must be included to explain why those data points were removed. In cases where data are included that were not part of the original outcome of the experiment they are considered *fabricated* results. Researchers must keep careful notation of all data records and account for how that data was collected. Any omissions that do not explain how results were obtained, either because of neglect or mistake or deliberately, can make the entire project invalid. In the event of neglecting to make a notation or simply making a mistake in the notation, immediate corrections should be made with a date stamp and the researcher's initials. A senior scientist should witness any addition or correction made to a record and include his or her initials and the date. The process of making appropriate corrections with more than one person present helps maintain the integrity of the results.

Interpretation of Data

In cases like the phone-texting speed experiment, in which the data involved differences between gender time speeds, the interpretation is straightforward; one is faster than the other or both genders text at roughly the same speed. However, not all data are as straightforward, especially when more than two groups are involved and some of the results are not always quantitative (see Chapter 3: Experimental Design). It is not unusual for the outcomes to be very close and the statistical analyses to be marginal, i.e., $p = .045$. In this situation, what decision should be made? It is always helpful to have a predetermined level of statistical significance, i.e., ≤ 05, so that the researcher can then make a decision by comparing the established or a priori level of significance to the statistical output, i.e., $p = .045$. In this case, the decision would be that there is a significant difference; however, that significant difference is marginal. Statistical analyses help make decisions about the hypotheses, but when several group comparisons are made, the researcher must examine the results both as a whole and individually. Experiments should be replicated (see Chapter 2: Defining Science and Chapter 4: Basic Statistics) to validate the results before reporting the results. Also, a researcher has the task of explaining what the results mean in the context of the hypothesis, i.e., it confirms or denies it, as well as within the available literature. How the data is interpreted, which forms the discussion of a manuscript, will direct or guide others who wish to follow new experimentation based on those results. The last statement must be taken with great responsibility and consciously followed because any evidence of purposely misleading others or falsifying results can lead to a multitude of consequences. Firstly, the trust bestowed upon scientists is comprised of the scientific community and society at-large. Secondly, replicating falsified results produces many wasted resources and losses of funds. Thirdly, losing a job or an entire career can impede any future scientific work. Lastly, there can be criminal charges that can lead to jail time. A good practice when reading the literature is to evaluate the results section first and derive one's own interpretation, then compare the notes to that of the author's interpretation. The reader can then make a determination if his or her interpretation lines up with that of the authors. If ideas do not align, there is no crime in that.

Plagiarism

Research requires much time, effort, and money in the hopes that the results provide novel information that can be published. When findings are reported in any form, the authors are responsible for avoiding plagiarism. What is plagiarism? Plagiarism is simply claiming credit or GW Copyeditorship of someone else's ideas. Plagiarism can be in the form of quoting text without crediting the source, not adequately paraphrasing, or attempting to publish results that have previously been published. Plagiarism in academics can be troublesome mostly as a result of lack of knowledge of how to adequately credit someone else's work when either quoting or paraphrasing. When using text directly from another source, that text must be in quotes (" ") and the citation given next to the quote.

> "*In the 17th century, many scientists kept new findings secret so that others could not claim the results as their own,*" On Being a Scientist: A Guide to Responsible Conduct in Research, 3rd edition, 2009.

Paraphrasing, however, summarizes a statement.

> A poor example of paraphrasing:
>
> *Many scientists in the 17th century deterred others from claiming their results as their own by keeping their findings secret.*
>
> This last example uses most of the same words but in a new order. This example would be considered plagiarism.
>
> A better example of paraphrasing:
>
> *It was common practice in the 1600s for scientists not to share their findings out of concern that their scientific findings or ideas would be stolen by colleagues.*

This example conveys the same idea without using the other author's exact wording. It provides the time period, describes who hid their findings, and why.

Plagiarism, like falsifying and fabrication, can lead to detrimental consequences that include job loss and even criminal charges. Much care and attention should be invested in verifying that any forms of communicating scientific results have the proper citation and appropriate credit given to the original author(s) or source(s).

Authorship

Once the data is collected and interpreted, the goal for any researcher is to publish his or her findings, primarily in a scientific journal. Other means of sharing findings is through institutional presentations or conferences in the form of oral presentations or posters. When authors submit their manuscripts to a scientific journal, decisions are made on who may be included as an author and in which order the authors will be included. The individuals who are listed as authors include those who participated in one form or another in the idea development, performing, experimenting, analyzing, interpreting, and writing of the manuscript. Listing an individual who took no part in any of the experiment is highly unethical. Scientific journal guidelines now ask what role each author played in the development of the findings.

Ordering of the Authors

"Who's on first" What's on Second, I Don't Know is on Third,"is a classic line from the Abbott and Costello comedy show. The decision to choose the order of the authors is not comical but rational and depends on the field of research. In most fields, the last author is normally the principle investigator or faculty member who runs the laboratory and the first author, though not in all cases, is highly credited for the ideas, experimentation, analysis, interpretation, and writing of the manuscript. The following authors should be listed by the amount of contribution they made during all stages of the research cycle (see Chapter 2: Defining Science). In certain circumstances, two or more individuals are credited with equal participation but are listed in alphabetical order. Any colleague that may have donated gifts that made the research possible should be listed in the Acknowledgments section (see Chapter 5: Scientific Literature). Individuals who assisted in editing the manuscript but did not play a role in the initial writing of the paper should also be listed in the Acknowledgments. The authors have a responsibility to disclose any conflicts of interest in the generation of the data, which may involve monetary, patents, or notoriety conflicts. A good rule of thumb and ethical practice to follow is for the researchers involved in the initial experimental stages to discuss the author order in the event the data is published.

Comportment in the Research Setting

Most research settings have a relaxed environment that does not require wearing suits or formal dress apparel. However, do not be deceived by the relaxed demeanor of the environment, because a display of professional behavior must be demonstrated at all times while on the premises where the research takes place, which includes indoors and outdoors. Most research these days happens in collaborative efforts that can include two or more colleagues from the same laboratory, department, or institution. Collaborations are also common between institutions. Unbecoming behavior can include disrespecting others' ideas or work. It is unethical to claim ideas and try to publish those ideas if they originated from someone else. In certain cases where meetings are held and ideas are bounced back and forth, a conversation must take place that clearly informs what intentions will be carried out if researchers intend to perform experiments or publish from those ideas. Always respect boundaries especially when the research occurs in laboratories and individuals are situated next to each other. If space is shared among colleagues, it is unethical to compromise another colleague's experiments by disturbing their research set up or compromising their experimental materials. Confidentiality of colleagues' work must be respected and should not be shared without the permission of the individual who claims copyright of that information. Also, only communicate and share data with individuals who are authorized or are participating in the research project. It is not only unethical but can also be unlawful to remove items from the research facility, which includes equipment (i.e., computers), supplies, or data except when given proper authorization. If the work was done through a collaborative effort, always include all of the collaborators at conference presentations and in manuscripts. A rule of thumb is to avoid gossip that can be harmful to another colleague or oneself if it gets around. Follow all safety precautions that are outlined by the Environmental and Safety Department. Any negligible behavior that results in violating safety rules can cause harm to others and oneself that can result in dismissal of the project and researchers charged with unlawful behavior. Research can bring great self-accomplishment when done ethically and respectfully while abiding by the rules and regulations.

Refresher

Truth is the foundation that requires all scientists to pursue their research interests with the utmost regard to standards and values including honesty, forthrightness, transparency, compassion, and fairness. Collaborations on research projects are more common today and require systems to be in place that ensure ethical behavior from all parties involved. The history of science has been tainted with cases that violated human and animal rights. These cases brought about policies and regulations at the national and international level. Among other rules, all research participants must provide consent to participate in a research project. Committees have been formed that oversee and report on human and animal treatment, such as the IRB and IACUC, respectively.

The management of data, whether developing an experimental design, collecting the data, including or excluding data, or interpreting data requires careful treatment to avoid fabricating or falsifying results. Historically, scientists have always concerned themselves with others claiming credit for their work, i.e., acts of plagiarism. Taking credit for someone else's research can lead to loss of career and sometimes even criminal charges. However, giving credit can also be too generous among colleagues when including someone as an author that did not play a significant role in the ideas, performing the experimentation, or contributing to the development of the manuscript. Scientific journals require that authors explain the role of each individual in the research that is listed as an author. How an individual behaves in the research setting can also define research conduct. A professional demeanor involves others' property and ideas, being conscious of surroundings, respecting boundaries, and avoiding gossip that can harm someone else's reputation. Appropriate behavior also includes following safety protocols and being careful, taking careful action to avoid harming oneself and others, and not removing any items from a research setting without proper authorization. Ethical behavior must be at the root of all scientific ventures to have a fulfilling experience in achieving discoveries and sharing those discoveries.

End-of-Chapter Exercises: Applying Concepts

1. Select one of the cases mentioned in Table 6.1, search the case on the internet and answer the following questions:
   A. When or during what time period did the research take place?
   B. Who were the subjects?
   C. What was the objective (goal) of the research?
   D. What did the researchers do to the subjects?
   E. How was it determined that the research was unethical?

    F. What law(s) or regulation(s), and/or agreements (reports) were developed as a consequence of the research?

    G. When did the law(s) or regulation(s) go into effect?

2. Can a person with good intentions expose themselves to unethical research behavior? Explain your answer.

References

National Institute of Environmental Health Sciences (NIEHS) (2015). *Institutional Review Board.* Retrieved from https://www.niehs.nih.gov/about/boards/irb/index.cfm

American Association for Laboratory Animal Science (AALAS) (2011). *The Institutional Animal Care and Use Committee (IACUC).* Retrieved from https://www.aalas.org/iacuc

World Medical Association (2017). *WMA Declaration of Helsinki—Ethical Principles for Medical Research Involving Human Subjects.* Retrieved from https://www.wma.net/policies-post/wma-declaration-of-helsinki-ethical-principles-for-medical-research-involving-human-subjects/

Chapter 7: Scientific Notebook

"Don't become a mere recorder of facts, but try to penetrate the mystery of their origin."

–Ivan Pavlov

Learning Objectives:

1. Explain why keeping a scientific notebook is important.
2. Explain what must be included in a scientific notebook.
3. Describe how to document in a scientific notebook.

If there is no record of how an experiment was conducted, can a scientist still publish the findings?

Keeping a Record—Why Is It Important?

Documentation dates back to ancient times when carvings on caves were the forms of communicating and expressing how life was lived in those times. Without those cave drawings, no knowledge would be known of those that walked this earth and how they lived. Why is it important to know who roamed this planet and what was life like then? It is important because it is part of the identity of those who roam the planet now and those who will come after. Knowledge of what was before guides the path to the future. Drawings on caves became writings on clay and over time became letters on paper, all of which are forms of documentation that communicate how things have developed or knowledge was gained (Mark, J.J., 2011).

Throughout history, scientists have concerned themselves with protecting their ideas and findings from colleagues but have also fought strongly at times to share their perspectives of novel phenomena during periods in which their views were rebuked and their writings outlawed from public access. From this knowledge, an appreciation can be fathomed of the significance in documenting and safeguarding *scientific writings*.

Credit

Historical events and scientific discovery records are filled with names and dates that can be overwhelming when attempting to memorize them for a course, but, those names and dates form a timeline, which can be thought of as a time capsule that, through documentation, transports those that come upon those writings through time and space. Scientific writing can be a guide that points in the direction to new findings. In that case, why are names important to document when only the dates matter? Recognition of those who carved out the paths is just as important as the periods in which they happened. Those individuals form part of the timeline, and it is not just their names attached to a date that matters; their discoveries are an extension of who the individuals were and what they believed in and stood for. The findings did not come about on their own, but through those individuals' beliefs. The persistence of one or several individuals who made those discoveries and their intuitive curiosity pointed others to where they should search for more novelty. Giving credit is not only about notoriety but is a historical document of the individual or individuals who dedicated themselves and who lead others to new discoveries, and that all starts with the *scientific notebook*.

Scientific Notebook

Several versions of the scientific notebook (i.e., *laboratory notebook* or *research notebook*) can be found at any store or online, though not any notebook can be used for scientific documentation. The scientific notebook has a specific format. The notebook should be a bound notebook, not spiraled, free of loose sheets of paper, and the size should accommodate the making of extensive entries, designs, or the adding of results that can be taped on the sheets. The sheets can be graph form or blank, white, lined sheets. The notebook should have a hardcover that will help protect the sheets inside from wear and tear, as well as a designated area for the date, project name, and volume. When initiating a new project, a new notebook should be used.

Structure

The notations that are entered into a scientific notebook follow a specific structure. The notations follow the scientific method (see Sample Notebook Template). All projects should start with a *title of the experiment* and a *date and time* when the project initiates. A *description of the overall project* and *objective* should be provided in one or two paragraphs. The description includes background and the rationale for why the project is relevant. The proposed hypothesis is then stated (see Chapter 3: Experimental Design). The experimental design follows the hypothesis statement. The experimental design includes the *methods* and *procedures* that are necessary to perform the experiment. The methods include the model that will be used if not involving humans. If a model is used, the details should be included; for example, if using a mouse model, the strain, age, and any special characteristic of that model that is unique should be included. If humans are the subjects, in that paragraph include the gender, age, and other details that are relevant to the participants. For example, if the study involves smokers, then the history of smoking should be included. Any requirements necessary for the participation in the research project should also be added, which is known as *inclusion criteria*. Also, if specific items are considered confounding to the experiment, these should be listed as *exclusion criteria*. The methods section also includes any materials and equipment required to carry out the experiment(s). The materials can include items that will be used to set up the experiment or used in the experiment. For example, if performing an experiment in a wet laboratory, materials can include vials, well plates, or sterile water. The size and number of each of the materials must be specified as well as the manufacturer from whom the supplies were bought. Also, the materials can include any solutions or chemicals and the quantities used. Although some materials are necessary to conduct the experiments, such as gloves, lab coats, and goggles, these items can be omitted. The procedures section describes how the experiment took place. The procedures can include a timeline and a thorough explanation of the process that was involved in completing the research. Rule of thumb: Include the research setting if the setting will influence the experimentation. It may be necessary to use biosafety level 3 or 4 facilities, which require a stringent sterile environment. Or the study may take place out in the field, at a hospital, or in a rehabilitative center. If the study involves hours or days, then include a table that reflects the times and steps that will take place.

Entries that should be done before initiating the experiment or study include the purpose of the study, the hypothesis, and the experimental design. If working with a team, each member's name should be included, and each person should review the notes and provide comments.

During the experiment, notations of any unexpected occurrences should be documented. For example, if a certain time-point was missed or circumstances beyond the experimenter's control happen, such as lights going out causing a disruption to the experiment, it must be noted. If the experiment involves humans and during the experiment a participant falls ill or decides to withdraw, that must be noted in the notebook with an explanation as to why that participant cannot complete the study. All notations must have a day and time entry with initials. Keep in mind that the notes should make sense and be understood by someone else that is not directly involved with the experiment but has knowledge of the research area.

Once the experiment has concluded and the data has been collected, the results can be entered into the notebook by taping a copy of the dataset to one of the sheets on the notebook labeled "Results." If any pictures or printouts were generated from specialized equipment, those should be taped into the journal. Any observations related to the results, such as pictures that did not have good resolution or values that are missing, a note should be included that addresses that issue. It is best to make a note or entry at the moment one is thinking about it rather than believe that it will be remembered later. The scientific notebook must have detailed accounts of the experiment, and details are not easily recalled at a later time. After entering or taping in all the results, explain each outcome in bullet form.

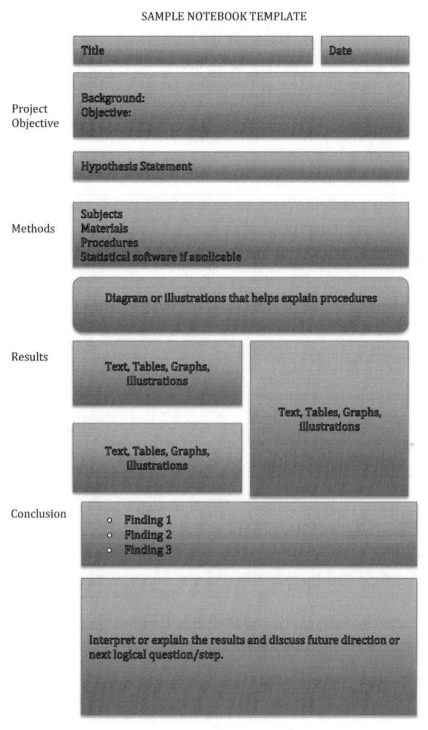

Figure 7.1 Sample Notebook Template

The conclusions are factual and objective, for example:

- With a 1° C temperature increase, enzyme activity increased by 15%.
- With drug treatment, an average of 20 words were memorized compared with an average of 10 words without drug treatment.
- Ten of 15 people continued with the therapeutic treatment for three months.

As shown in the examples, the conclusions state the results but do not explain the results. The results can then be interpreted in paragraph form and provide interpretations and explanations of the results. Any unexpected outcomes can also be listed in the conclusion and followed with an explanation as to why those results may have occurred. If the experiment is concluded, a couple of suggestions for future projects can be added to conclude the project's entries. If the same project will be continued with follow up experiments, then continue making entries to the same journal on subsequent clean sheets and a new title. A new journal must be used if initiating a different project. A well-organized notebook permits easy referencing and verification of entries. To help keep the notebook organized, on the left side of the pages write labels with objective, hypothesis, experimental design, methods, results, and conclusions.

What is included in the scientific notebook?

The scientific journal represents a record that delineates the scientific thought process of the person that is journaling and becomes a permanent record of those thoughts. In addition to all scientific notes and the date and time when the notation was entered, the journal should have the names of the individuals who took part in the experiment. It is common to use abbreviations when entering notes though this practice can prevent other individuals from understanding the notes. A list of acronyms is suggested to help decipher any abbreviations. Always keep in mind that the journal should be a record that can be referred to, not just for the present experiment, but also in the future. When extended experiments are documented, each page should be numbered. Also, include the author, date, and title of articles that were referred to in the background or experimental design. Web links can be documented if the information from the website was of scientific value to the experiment. Having a record of the references or links can facilitate the writing process or when preparing presentations on a later date. If more than one notebook was necessary, label each volume in chronological order. Because the idea is to keep the journal as a permanent record, always use black ink and never use pencil. Over time, pencil markings will fade and can easily be erased. If a mistake is made, do not use white out. Cross out the mistake with one line and initial and date next to the line. Make a notation where items can be found.

For example:

Serum vials 25 µg in -80° F freezer top shelves in labeled blue box.

The more details of where items are located will ease the search, especially if a number of freezers are used or several boxes of the same color are stored with similar specimens. When making notations of human studies, note any information that was obtained by local medical institutions or government in the event concerns arise that require follow up information with medical facilities or governmental agencies. The more details and supporting documents that are included, the more complete the journal will be, and it will be easier to replicate the findings contained within.

What is not included in the scientific notebook?

The scientific journal is a legal document that provides information and scientific findings and should not contain markings such as doodles or jokes. Protocols should not be rewritten or taped in the journal but stored in a separate notebook. If a modification is made to a protocol, then enter a document in the notebook that states that the protocol was modified and explain why the modification was made. Keeping a neat and well-organized journal helps others follow the information as it is intended.

Scientific Notebook

Although the notations entered in a scientific notebook are from individuals performing the experiments, the notebook is not the property of those individuals. The scientific notebook belongs to the institution where the research takes place. The institution can be a university or college. Also, governmental agencies that have research facilities keep the notebooks of their scientists. The notebook must remain in the laboratory. What if the research takes place in the field? When the research takes place outside the facilities, the notebook can accompany the person performing the entries and should be returned to the institution after completion of the study.

Refresher

The scientific notebook represents a person's thought process and approach to discovering novel phenomenon. In most disciplines, scientific notebook entries will follow the scientific method. The notebook should be treated as any other official document; it should not contain any irrelevant information such as doodles or jokes. If the research project involves more than one person, all those involved should be listed in the notebook entry. Furthermore, any references that are used as part of the background or experimental design should be noted. The content of the notebook is a permanent record that belongs to the institution that supports the research and is not the propriety of the individual that maintains it.

End-of-Chapter Exercises: Applying Concepts

1. Explain the significance of maintaining an accurate and detailed scientific notebook.
2. Following the slime recipe in Textbox 7, create a mock scientific notebook entry. Refer to the chapter text and sample notebook entry for all required information that must be included and that which should be omitted. Have fun!

Elmer's Recipe for Colored Slime

Supplies Needed:

½ Tbsp. of baking soda

1 Tbsp. of contact lens solution

4 fl. oz. Elmer's White school glue

Your choice of food coloring

Instructions:

1. Pour the entire bottle glue into a bowl.

2. Add ½ Tbsp. of baking soda and mix thoroughly.

3. After mixing, add your choice of food coloring until you get the color you want.

4. Add 1 Tbsp. of contact lens solution.

5. Mix until mixture gets harder to mix and slime begins to form.

6. Take the slime out and begin kneading with both of your hands.

7. If needed, add ¼ Tbsp. of contact lens solution to make the slime less sticky.

*Adult supervision is required. This project is not appropriate for children under the age of three years. Always wash your hands before and after making and playing with slime. Warning: If large quantities of contact lens solution are accidentally ingested (greater than a tablespoon), get medical attention immediately.

References

Mark, J. J. (2011). Writing. *Ancient History Encyclopedia.* Retrieved from https://www.ancient.eu/writing/

Chapter 8: Communicating Science Through Presentations

"If you can't explain it simply, you don't understand it well enough."–Albert Einstein

Learning Objectives:

1. Explain the significance of scientific presentations.

2. Distinguish the different scientific presentation forums.

3. Recognize the differences and similarities between a scientific poster and an oral presentation.

4. Prepare a scientific presentation for the intended audience.

In the initial stages of preparing a scientific presentation, what is the first thing to consider?

Introduction

Sharing information comes naturally to people except when it happens while standing on a stage. Presenting scientific material can be an exciting event for the novice when sharing research projects. Although sharing scientific findings can be intimidating to the novice, a sense of satisfaction can overcome those unsettling feelings when he or she knows that the ideas and supporting information shared originates from contributions made by the speaker, i.e., you. Imagine having the knowledge of an existing treasure of incredible wealth that no one knows about except one person, is that treasure's worth significant? If one is seeking scientific quests without the intention of informing others, the scientific quest can be a futile effort. From the start of the scientific inquiry, the goal should be to communicate the findings. The value in sharing novel findings opens up channels to receive feedback and foster new ideas. Keeping in mind that although experiments can come to an end, science continues with new questions that develop from novel findings.

Chapter 5: Scientific Literature describes the organization of scientific literature that starts with writing the manuscript and ends with a published article. In contrast to the written form of communication, verbal communications, such as oral (spoken) presentations, are an effective form of disseminating scientific information. Oral presentations, like scientific literature, also follow a specific structure and organization. The process from the initial experiment planning to publication can be lengthy at times, spanning the course of years. While the written communication may take a while before the findings are published, scientific findings can be shared both formally and informally through oral presentations or other communications. Informal communications most often take place in settings that are less structured and that are in the form of brief updates or reports. Furthermore, presentations that are informal are projects that are in the initial stages of experimentation and in progress.. Formal communications are structured, organized, and intended to communicate proposed hypotheses and findings from experiments that test hypotheses. Formal presentations are ongoing intradepartmental presentations or take place at scientific conferences where scientists congregate and share their findings.

The novice's first informal scientific communication most often involves providing updates in a laboratory setting and/or classroom. More formal scientific communications are in the form of a poster or an oral presentation that are usually presented to the home institution or at a conference. Presenting scientific material can be nerve-wracking, especially when presenting for the first time. The following guidelines will facilitate the process to create professional and memorable scientific presentations.

The Audience

The first thing to ask before preparing a presentation is: Who are the attendees, i.e., the audience? The venue can determine the makeup of the audience. Scientific meetings where scientists meet to share their research are referred to as scientific conferences. Small- or medium-size conferences can comprise approximately 100 to a few thousand attendees and may take place over two to three days. In contrast, large conferences may have up to thirty thousand attendees and can be a weeklong event. The attendees converge from different universities that are composed of individuals from private industry and academics. Undergraduates also attend larger conferences under the mentorship of a faculty or senior laboratory member. A symposium is also a conference that is a more focused on meeting compared with a conference where broader areas of research are embodied. Scientific symposiums, similar to conferences, can take place at the home institution or at a different venue. If the presentation is part of a symposium organized by the home institution, that will include undergraduates, graduate students, faculty from various departments or colleges and, in some cases, administrators. Another type venue that is intended for a nonscientific audience and aims to inform the general public is public arenas. Individuals from profit or nonprofit organizations, in addition to individuals from the community, attend these general public presentations. The venue and type of meeting will inform about the makeup of the audience that will be in attendance. Whether the audience is academic or not, they are invested in learning about the science.

The Presentation's Technical Level

The most significant part in preparing a presentation lies with the audience's level of expertise, which defines the presentation's technical level. The technical level refers to the terms or language used in reference to the content presented. The presentation's technical terminology level can be substantial to an audience with substantial amount of expertise in the field. Keep in mind that even though the audience may have expertise, only the necessary technical terms should be used with brief explanations to expand on the terminology. In contrast, when presenting to members of the community, layman's terms should be used with fewer technical terms and more thorough explanations of scientific terms. The content's depth and breadth also depend on the level of expertise of the audience. The less familiar an audience is with the topic, the presentation will cover breadth more so than depth. For an audience with a higher level of expertise, however, the content can be presented more in depth.

Presentation Software Programs

In the market, roughly 40 types of programs are available that are designed to create presentations. In this chapter, two programs most often used in academia and students prefer for their friendly user capabilities are Prezi and PowerPoint. The basic instructions or steps to preparing a presentation apply to any software program. PowerPoint may be best for classroom presentations, which are brief (under ten minutes), and for laboratory meetings when presenting project updates. Presentations longer than ten minutes can use both Prezi and PowerPoint to achieve a professional and succinct presentation.

In the following paragraphs, brief descriptions of Prezi and PowerPoint are offered; however, more extensive tutorials are available from the software programs' websites, and there are helpful tutorials at www.youtube.com.

Prezi

Prezi, a web-based presentation program highly recognized for its zooming features, adds an appeal that enlivens the presentation. Prezi can be organized into major topics or categories and then details can be added to each category. When presenting each category, the zooming function of Prezi helps focus in on details and zoom out to appreciate the overall categories and organization of the presentation. Prezi does require logging in to the Prezi website (www.prezi.com) with free access. However, the presentations are created within the site; therefore, Prezi requires an Internet connection to gain access to the program without the downloadable features that are available with the free access version.

PowerPoint

PowerPoint does not require extensive training to use; however, it is recommended that following tutorial videos can be time efficient and alleviate any frustrations while developing the presentation. PowerPoint has several templates that the designer can start off from or a blank slide from which to build. The slides can be transitioned from one slide to the next using the keyboard or a slide changer remote. The program contains templates that facilitate adding graphics or illustrations. PowerPoint has several font types and presentation graphics from which to choose to make the presentation suit the topic. With PowerPoint, it is easy to add a hyperlink to direct the presentation to a webpage or video and then return to the presentation. Once the presentation is finalized, it can be projected onto a larger screen from the computer or saved on a memory stick for convenient mobility.

Length of Presentation

Things to consider when deciding the length of the slide are allotted presentation time and the amount of information necessary to achieve a cohesive story. The length of the presentation does not necessarily determine the number of slides, however, the time spent on each slide is a factor. The duration of the presentation varies depending on the objective of the presentation. For example, presentations that take place in the classroom can range from three to 15 minutes. These presentations can be presented individually or in groups. Presentations that are between 15 and 30 minutes can take place within a group of colleagues in a laboratory that will have more details about the background of the project, its experimentation, and its findings. Also, taking a higher level or graduate course may at times require a presentation of this length. A presentation in the 45- to 60-minute range is normally presented to a department or at a conference. A presentation longer than 60 minutes is ascribed to experts such as keynote speakers at institutions or conferences. A keynote speaker is an expert with a long career scientific trajectory and extended network. The keynote speaker offers extensive experience and knowledge converging those two to deliver the bigger picture ideas and major themes of a conference.

The novice's first presentations range between four to ten minutes and are normally prepared for weekly laboratory meetings. The key points and principles in preparing a presentation are applicable to all presentations. No matter how long a presentation will be, the audience demographic (or makeup) and what the key points the presenter wishes the audience would walk away with after the presentation should be kept in mind.

How to Organize the Presentation

Storytelling Organization

Background

The first slide should state why the following slides are important. The first slide should answer the question: *Why should the audience take interest in the presentation?* Once the "why it matters" slide has been developed, the following slides build from that premise. Telling the audience they should care about the forest because it is part of nature and all humans should have some stake in the matter is not a convincing point, however true the point might be. The presenter must make a case as to why the experimentation was necessary and why the audience should be engaged in what will follow. The background includes information from published literature that will help put the new findings into context. Established ideas or theories are explained in the background slides that establish or build up why the research was pursued in the first place. Is the new research establishing a new theory after ruling out other theories, or is the experimentation introducing more evidence to an existing theory? The content of the background will address the latter question. The first few slides are dedicated to the background. How many slides are used depends on how much background will be covered. This information can be determined by how much time is allotted for the presentation.

Methods

The methods part of the presentation follows the background that describes how the study was performed. The methods slides contain information about the subjects, materials, and procedures. The subjects refer to either humans or the use of a model. Human subjects are referred to as the participants and a description of the inclusions and exclusions that comprised the study cohort. A description will include the age, gender, socioeconomic background and any other details that explain why that specific cohort was used for the research project. However, if the study involved models (either computers or animals) then those are described as well with details that explain why that specific model was appropriate for the study. To ensure that pertinent materials are mentioned, as a guide ask, "Would a person understand the results if that specific method was not mentioned?" Leave out any materials that do not need to be mentioned, for example, the use of lab coats or gloves. When in doubt, put it to the test, "Would the audience understand the results without mention of the gloves or lab coats?" The answer is yes, i.e., the audience will be able to follow just fine without having to mention those two items. However, items that should be mentioned include the special equipment that was used, the duration of the experiment, the setting where the experiment took place, and the type of study, for example, a longitudinal or cross-sectional study. If statistics were used, explain how the data was collected and analyzed.

New Findings

The novel findings can be displayed in graphic form using figures and/or tables. Bulleted points can be used along with the graphics. Describe the findings in as much detail, such as: Are there trends going up or down? Are findings revealing the presence of a substance, a protein, or a behavior not previously detected or present? How are the findings significant? Explain the findings within the context of the working theory, i.e., is the theory confirmed or disconfirmed? Keep statements objective, avoiding opinions about the results.

Conclusions and Future Directions

A short summary of the major points helps refresh and reinforce the novel findings. The audience received an abundance of information over a very short period of time, which makes it difficult for the audience to recall or keep track of all the information. Putting extensive findings in bullet points and briefly reiterating each point will help reinforce the overall objective of the project and will help transition to the next slide, "Future Directions. " With a Future Directions slide, explain the questions that developed from the research project or gaps that remain unaddressed. The proposed future directions should be specific and guide the audience to envision the next research project. If already working on those projects, mention that ongoing studies are currently being performed to address those questions. A concluding statement that ties it all together and projects the bigger picture completes the presentation.

Title or Cover Page

Presentation programs have a template for the first slide. The typical first slide information includes the presenters' names, title of the presentation, institution that the presenters belong to, and the date. The cover slide has preprogrammed settings for the font size and style but can be changed to suit the presentation. The title should resonate with the audience. Some titles can have light humor to grab the audience attention and intrigue while others may have a more serious tone. If the topic, for example, covers material on war-stricken children suffering from malnutrition, humor may not be appropriate. However, if the content involves detailed molecular mechanisms, to spark the audience's attention, light humor may be appropriate. Take into consideration the topic's subject matter and the audience when making decisions about whether to add humor.

Text

The audience's attention should be directed and guided by the presenter. Most novices will feel intimidated and somewhat exposed while standing in front of people and become so afraid that they forget the material. Consequently, the slides will comprise too much text. Too much text with extensive sentences or long sentences that take up more than one line on the slide or paragraphs of text is a recipe for losing an audience. The text should serve only as a guide and not narrate the presentation. Bullet points can be used to help organize the topics in a chronological or logical order.

For example, bullet points:

Don't:

- Over 100 years ago in 1882, Mycobacterium tuberculosis was discovered by Robert Koch.
- Mycobacterium tuberculosis is the bacteria that causes tuberculosis and can lead to death if not treated.
- Mycobacterium tuberculosis is also known as an opportunistic infection because if the immune system is compromised, the bacteria can readily infect both the peripheral and central nervous system. For example, when a person is infected with HIV, he or she will also develop tuberculosis.

Do:

- Mycobacterium Tuberculosis identified by Robert Koch
- An opportunistic infectious agent
- Co-morbidity with HIV

The Don'ts are overwhelming with information with lengthy sentences that will easily distract an audience. The Do's are short, concise phrases that allow the presenter to elaborate on each bullet point. The presenter should direct the attention of the audience to each specific bullet point and expand on it. How does the presenter remember all of the material when several pairs of eyes are staring back? Practice, practice, and more practice. Most preferably, practice with family and friends; they can be very supportive, and if the material is clear to them, it will be clear to the intended audience. Why? If the ideas are clear and translatable to individuals that know nothing about the topic (naïve audience), then an audience with some familiarity with the research area will capture the ideas just as well. While practicing, the time spent on each slide should be recorded to ensure that the length of the presentation will fall within the allotted time for the presentation. Always use a laser pointer to guide the audiences and to help explain the illustrations. Once rehearsed well enough, transitioning from one slide to the next will appear seamless.

Character Size

The character size of the text should be big enough so that individuals sitting at a distance can read the bullet points. Most facilities that are designed for presentations will already have an appropriately sized screen on which the presentation will be projected. As the presenter, inquire, or if possible, visit the room to gain an idea of how large the font will need to be so that it will be visible from the audience sitting at the back of the room. A recommended character size is no less than 28; however, this may depend on the type of font used. Avoid adding bullet points at the bottom of the slide because the audience may not be able to view them. The templates will help guide the content of the slide to avoid having text cut off from the screen on the right or left side. Avoid using acronyms, or if you need to use an acronym, spell the acronym out the first time it is used and explain that the acronym will be used from that point on. The ideas should transfer to the audience in a manner that the audience can follow the presentation without having to read lengthy sentences or struggle to keep up with the narrator.

Illustrations

A picture is worth a thousand words. Illustrations help the audience follow and assimilate the presented material; it helps convey the intended ideas in the manner that the presenter intended the audience to perceive them. The use of illustrations helps the presenter project the tone, the ideas, or the instructions in a straightforward manner. The illustrations can be shown alone or paired with bullet points. The presenter should use illustrations as a tool to convey the ideas and not as a replacement for the presenter's narratives. When it is necessary for more than one illustration to be on a slide, it is best to keep it under three illustrations, otherwise the slide will be too busy and confuse the audience. If the message can be conveyed with an illustration, go with it. Do not presume that by showing the illustration the audience will capture the significance of the image but take time to guide the audience through the illustration.

Animations

Taking it a notch higher, the text and illustrations can be animated to facilitate a presentation that is well thought-out and organized. In the event several bullet points are used, the text can be animated to appear one at a time. Having text appear as the presenter speaks helps keep the audience focused on what is presented. A picture can have an animation to express the ideas in the form of action on the screen rather than a two-dimensional illustration. Presentation tools are to make a presentation easier to follow. When too much animation is used, it can have the opposite effect where the audience may end up confused and lose interest, and the same applies to sound effects. Careful consideration should be taken with the animation tools to deliver a presentation that directs attention and informs. Similar to adding an animation, on occasion a video can be incorporated to facilitate the message; however, videos should be embedded into the presentation to avoid lags during the presentation, and it is recommended to keep them as short as possible, especially for short presentations. The function of adding a video is to support the overall message, not to be the presentation.

References

When citing a source in a presentation, it is best to cite the reference on the slide where the information is mentioned. The reference should be in smaller font and at the bottom of the slide. However, when more than one reference is mentioned on a slide, the references can be shown below the text or illustration that is referenced. To avoid excessive information on one slide, keep to a maximum of three references on one slide.

Acknowledgments

A scientific presentation includes a slide that acknowledges direct and indirect sources that contributed to the research. An acknowledgment slide titled, "Acknowledgments," will list the names of all the individuals that contributed to the project in any significant manner, such as providing a gift that helped perform the experimentation. Anyone that collaborated with the project, e.g., faculty, postdocs, and graduate students that helped supervise the project and also contributed to ideas should be mentioned. Also included on this slide are the organizations that funded the research. The funding reference number is noted next to the funding source. The affiliations or institutions that collaborated are also credited on this slide. Simply put, this is the "Thank You" slide.

Delivery

When watching someone on stage, what about him or her captures your attention? Does the person on stage look at the audience directly? Are they animated? Does the presenter project his or her voice across the room? The presenter can do a number of things to capture the audience's attention, especially for a lengthy presentation. Opening with a question attracts the audience's attention toward the speaker and engages the audience to actively participate. A joke at the beginning of the presentation can captivate the audience and create a relaxing atmosphere. While presenting, a short pause of a few seconds helps the audience follow the presentation. A pause can also indicate that a new topic will ensue. Becoming overwhelmingly nervous can be counterproductive and have a "freezing" effect on the presenter. The presenter can freeze up by remaining motionless and standing in the exact spot from beginning to the end, holding on to the microphone for dear life, and staring either at the wall, at one person, or at one side of the room. An antidote to freezing while presenting is practicing beforehand. While practicing the talk, also rehearse the following: 1) Scan the room back and forth with short pauses ensuring that visual direction projects toward each side of the room where the audience sits; 2) while scanning the room, walk across the stage when not directing the audience to the screen; 3) project your voice toward the back of the room, using a microphone if needed; 4) guide the audience to the screen when addressing a new bullet point or describing an illustration, then direct your attention back to the audience; 5) when possible, request that a screen be available at the back of the room to avoid turning away from the audience, and 6) keep track of how much time is spent on each slide to ensure the presentation meets the required time allotted. With enough practice all of the former points will assimilate to deliver a fluid and seamless presentation. Lastly, much effort was invested by the time the presentation is delivered, so get excited and that will convey a genuine interest to the audience.

Voiceovers and Video Presentations

Presentations are becoming more common in the classroom setting. Students may be required to prepare a presentation to their peers or prepare a presentation in the form of a video using special programs designed to prepare presentations. PowerPoint and Prezi both have voiceovers to help design presentations with narration. There are other features that can be incorporated, such as a pointer while narrating the presentation with a voiceover. These types of presentations facilitate distance learning such as online courses. PowerPoint voiceover instructions are straightforward depending on the type of operating system using the PowerPoint selection can find the audio record feature. On a personal computer, recording a voiceover can be done in two ways: Under the tab INSERT, select "Audio" on the right top corner, select "Record" and start the narration. Or, select the SLIDE SHOW tab, select "Record slide show" and click on "Start recording from current slide." A small box will display, check mark "Narrations, ink, and laser pointer." Once the narration is complete, just click on the icon and a small speaker will appear on the right lower side of the slide that indicates the narration was recorded. When the slide comes up, the narration automatically starts. On a Macintosh, on the top bar menu select the INSERT tab, then scroll down to "Audio" and select "Record audio." A window will appear with a red button labeled "Record," select the button, and start speaking. After completing the narrative, select "Save" and a speaker icon will appear on the slide (Figure 8.1). For more detailed instructions, numerous voiceover tutorials are accessible at www.youtube.com, with step-by-step instructions on creating voiceovers.

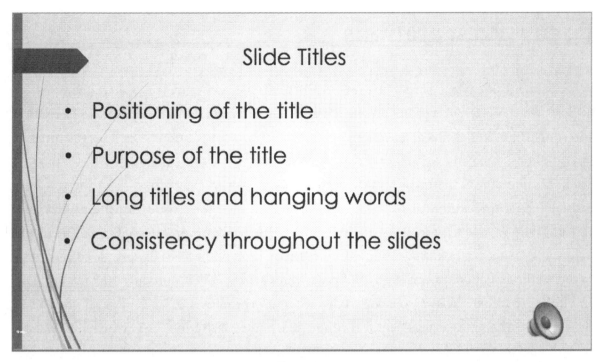

Figure 8.1

With the expanding online courses offered by universities and colleges in addition to the booming social media outlets, presentations via video are now common avenues to communicate scientific material. Scientific content is easily accessible by uploading to websites like YouTube or Open Video Project (www.open-video.org). The Open Video Project website focuses on educational videos with an academic emphasis, whereas YouTube video uploads are open to all topics. Preparing a video can be done using any device that has a video feature with audio. Although the preparation of a video may take place in a private setting, the experience can produce nervousness. Trying to keep focused while recording and speaking at the same time requires skill. Trying to remember all of the points while staring at the camera piece can be challenging, but with a prepared script a flawless narrative can be delivered. The script should not be in view while the video runs, and it should not be too obvious that you are reading from a script. The script can be placed right below or above the camera.

Preparing a video can be as nerve-wracking as standing in front of an audience. Voices may become softer or lower. Soft-voiced tones may be enhanced by increasing the volume on the device. If the recording is too loud, the volume can always be turned down rather than have issues with inaudible sound. Practice a few times and review the video to make sure you are looking straight ahead at the camera lens and avoid shifting the head left, right, up, or down, which may appear as if you are searching for something.

Poster Presentations

When students are participating in a research project, they get a chance to share the research by preparing a poster. The poster will have an introduction and background, methods, results, and conclusion. Sometimes an abstract is included. Each of these different sections mirrors the format of designing an experiment (Figure 8.2). Similar to scientific literature (see Chapter 5: Scientific Literature), the organization starts with an abstract that summarizes the research project. The introduction (or background) opens with the broader ideas of the project and explains the gaps that exist in the current literature. The logical order starts with what is known followed by what is not known leading to the theory or hypothesis of the proposed research. In the methods section, the materials and procedures are explained, and they can take up a fair amount of space on a poster. Keeping to the necessary methods used and followed provides a clear picture of how the experiment was conducted. Some illustrations can be included to help explain the methodology. The results section will demonstrate the figures with text that elaborate the figures (captions). This section explains the outcomes of the experiment and reports statistical analyses. In the conclusion, the key points are stated in bulleted form. The key points should be kept aligned with the overall objective of the research to avoid listing excessive points that are not relevant. Any sources that were referenced are listed under the conclusions in chronological order. In-text citations should be noted to indicate where the sources were referenced. When citing references, use the American Psychological Association (APA) for referencing both in-text and reference list items. The acknowledgments section is the last section of the poster. Under the acknowledgments, credit the funding sources and any colleagues who contributed with gifts or provided support but were not directly involved with the experiments.

Dimensions

Before starting to build the different sections of the poster, first consider the dimensions of the poster. The dimensions of a poster do vary, though 36" × 48", 42" × 60", and 48" × 48" (length × width) are typical poster dimensions. The specifics on poster dimensions and requirements can be obtained by following the presentation's guidelines. These guidelines can be found on the sponsor's website or can be obtained directly from the event's organizing committee or personnel.

Software and Printing

PowerPoint can be used to design a poster because the margins can be adjusted to fit the dimensions on one slide. Alternatively, Microsoft Word or Illustrator can be used to design a poster. In all three software programs the electronic poster can be saved as a .pdf and transferred to a memory stick. The poster can be printed at the home institution printing shop or at a professional printing shop; the quality of the paper and its dimensions will determine the cost of printing. Posters that have a glossy texture have a nice appearance but the cost may be higher. Also, the amount of color graphics or background included in the poster will affect printing cost. The cost to print posters is usually supported by grant funding or departmental funds; however, approval from the mentor or department must first be obtained before starting to prepare the poster. If funding comes from a scholarship, those funds most likely will cover the printing cost. When picking up the poster, use a poster-carrying tube to safeguard the poster and avoid damaging the poster during transport.

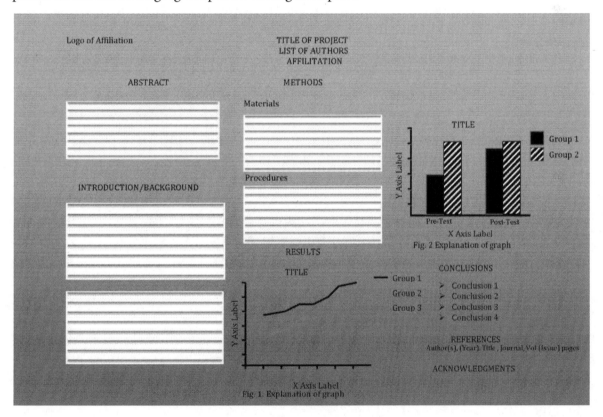

Figure 8.2

Refresher

Scientific presentations form a story that includes a background, new information, and future direction. The significance of a treasure's worth depends on the awareness that it exists. Similarly, the significance of scientific findings diminishes if not shared and communicated. The initial steps in preparing a scientific presentation start with the audience. Familiarizing oneself with the makeup of the audience and time allotted to present will help determine how much material to include and the level of technicality the presentation will require.

Various software programs are available to help prepare presentations, and the choice of software is contingent on the objective of the presentation. The two most commonly used programs for scientific presentations are Prezi and PowerPoint, and both programs are user friendly. Learning how to use these programs can be easily achieved with numerous video tutorials available on YouTube. The presentation should be organized with bullet points and illustrations in such a way that guides the audience to unravel the scientific story. Acknowledgement of individuals and funding sources is on the last slide. Practicing helps overcome nervousness associated with public speaking. Minding eye contact, head turning, and body movements while rehearsing the content of the presentation creates an immaculate delivery. Using presentation software such as PowerPoint to create voiceovers can be an alternative an addition to in-person scientific communications. Voiceover presentations are useful in that the presentation can be narrated by guiding the audience point by point with bullet points and illustrations.

Posters are another form of sharing scientific information at home institutions or conferences. A poster presentation shares information that can be preliminary and an avenue to receive feedback. The poster presentations follow the scientific method, i.e., telling a story with a background, novel findings, and future direction. Similar to an oral presentation, first consider who are the attendees and inquire about the poster dimensions . PowerPoint can be used to prepare posters by adjusting the margins and formatting the printing specifications. With adequate preparation, whether the presentation setting is formal or informal, the novice can deliver a professional and well-informed presentation.

End-of-Chapter Exercises: Applying Concepts

1. Explain the differences between an informal and formal scientific presentation and in what types of forums each are normally performed.

2. Define and explain each of the sections of a scientific presentation.

3. Create a voiceover presentation using Prezi or PowerPoint with the following specifications:

   a. Keeping with the same topic, prepare a five and 15-minute presentation.

   b. Keeping with the same topic, prepare the presentation for a laboratory meeting audience and a nonscientific (general public) audience.

   c. The presentation should include a minimum of two illustrations and one animation.

   d. For the 15-minute presentation only, include a two-minute video.

Chapter 9: Group Work

"You cannot teach a man anything; you can only help him discover it in himself."

–Galileo Galilei

Learning Objectives:

1. Explain what is considered group work.
2. Identify and describe the various group dynamics within a group.
3. Explain effective group work strategies.

Academic Success

Seeking higher education comes with excitement and adventure for the new student. Students walking into higher education institutions come in with good intentions to perform well and achieve academic success. However, when a student is not well-informed, what strategies and setting realistic goals can blur the motivation to achieve academic success? Creating an understanding of what implies academic success is a good first start on the path to achieving it. Academic success, aside from finishing a degree plan and having good grades, can also imply feelings of self-achievement and grasping new knowledge. What is meant by self-accomplishment? A sense of accomplishment refers to achieving or reaching some point or level that can apply to a milestone or obtaining an understanding of ideas or concepts. Self-accomplishment can refer to those instances that are referred to as "Eureka" or "I get it" moments. It also applies having a self-awareness of how to perceive views that have been transformed through gaining new knowledge. For example, a novice researcher may achieve self-accomplishment when he or she designs the first experiment, writes the first scientific paper, or presents for the first time. All of these challenges—designing experiments, writing a scientific paper, and presenting for the first time—pose a great sense of challenge but once attempted, feelings of satisfaction can stir inside the person. Those feelings represent a sense of accomplishment because new knowledge has been achieved. The process of gaining new knowledge leads to new learning experiences.

Strategies for Academic Success

When starting college, students quickly learn that there is much more freedom when managing schedules, as opposed to high school where the entire day is programmed. Coming to this realization can cause uncomfortable feelings. In college, the student must be proactive in keeping up with each course's assignments as well as study time. A sense of being overwhelmed can be experienced when entering large classrooms, which are standard for first-year students. Being aware that it is normal to feel overwhelmed is part of starting something new, and those feelings fade once the student is settled into a new routine. Instructors can assist in clarifying any confusion or questions about the expectation of the course. When the student feels nervous about approaching an instructor, he or she should e-mail the instructor. Keep in mind that other students are also going through the same feelings and are also adjusting to the new environment. Striking up conversations with peers while in line at the bookstore or food court can help relieve the pressure of the first few days. Starting an academic training begins the opportunity for students to create experiences that will be intellectually stimulating, challenging, and fulfilling. In the first week of the semester, take time to review each syllabus and jot down all of the pertinent dates and deadlines to help alleviate overwhelmed feelings. Think about the goals of each course and how the instructor has laid out the syllabus to accomplish the learning objectives. Spend some time in the first few days examining the topics, readings, quizzes, or other assignments. Taking some time to think about how to organize and approach each course is referred to as "thinking about how to think" or *metacognition*.

Metacognition

Similar to trying to put together a piece of furniture that arrived in a box without reading the instructions, the task becomes tougher and will most likely result in more work, resulting in a frustrating experience. Taking the time to read through instructions and laying out all the pieces and visualizing how each piece will form the larger piece symbolizes metacognition. In applying metacognition, an awareness of the goals becomes clearer while organizing and thinking about how to approach each goal. Metacognition can save time and effort when effectively applied. Taking a few moments before starting a task and thinking through how that task will be approached results in better outcomes than when jumping straight into a task without any planning. Metacognition involves taking an active role in the learning process.

Active Learning

"Active" refers to something that the learner does and not something that an instructor does for the learner. Active learning promotes grasping information that goes beyond memorization. The learner engages in the learning process by using his or her sense of sight, hearing, touch, and smell to grasp concepts and new information. Active learning involves having the ability to explain terminology beyond definitions and demonstrates how those terms apply in a bigger picture, similar to the pieces of furniture that form one larger piece. With active learning, a change in how an individual thinks and views information happens through the process of acquiring new information. Active learning can take place in the classroom as well as outside the classroom.

Classroom Instruction

Classroom instruction has traditionally involved an instructor or professor standing in front of the room talking to the students and sometimes prompting students with questions. The instructor usually writes notes on a board or has a PowerPoint with bullet points and illustrations. When this approach of lecturing is used, the students mainly focus on what is written in front of them, busily taking notes or copying the text from the PowerPoint with little attention to the instructor's explanations that help expand their concept of the material. The energy required to both listen and copy notes can be an exhaustive effort, and often pertinent information is missed. Also, students will be more prone to try to memorize the information when the information given follows bulleted points. The lecture approach, with the exception of a handful of students that actively participates in class, leaves students out of the learning experience and without the depth required to help understand how the information fits together into the overall objectives of the course. An interactive classroom or learning environment, however, engages students in solving problems and helps them actively search for definitions on their own to solve problems—this is the process of active learning. In addition, working with peers in groups can stimulate active learning through engaging in discussions and voicing differences of how the information was perceived, all of which requires proactive participation in the learning process.

Group Work in the Classroom

Active learning can be most satisfying and fulfilling when learning new material with peers or in groups. Study groups are formed when students get together after school and study for a test or just meet to study their own assignments. These study groups, or group work, can be incorporated into the classroom permitting students to work with each other on course assignments. This approach of completing assignments avoids having students sit in a classroom for 50 minutes or more only note-taking and not having the opportunity to stop and think about the material. Working in groups in the classroom has an added benefit of providing access to the instructor. The instructor can enhance the learning experience by assigning group work that requires the students to think more thoroughly about the material and helps them apply the terms to achieve a bigger picture.

Advantages

A number of advantages are possible when participating in group work to complete assignments. First-year students can experience a sense of isolation, especially in large universities. Students that are underrepresented tend to feel most isolated in academic institutions where the perception of intense competition is felt. Working in groups can overcome feelings of isolation and help create an academic environment that is less intimidating and can have a positive impact on academic success.

Working with peers allows for different perspectives to be voiced in a safe environment. Also, the grasp of novel material can be obtained with much more ease and less frustration. Forming groups lessens the burden of having deadlines pile up by sharing the responsibility and distributing tasks to complete projects or working through the entire project together. Also, missing deadlines can be avoided when peers hold each other responsible for handing in the assignments on time.

Disadvantages

There are some disadvantages when working in groups that are usually the causes for ineffective group work. Students may not share the work equally, and that can create feelings of resentment among the students. When students fail to assume their responsibilities within a group a shifting occurs creating stress on other members. Motivation to complete assignments is the main factor that can be disproportionately distributed among a group. Some students will be more motivated than others for a number of reasons; for example, students may be well-prepared for the course, find the course material exciting, or be on financial support, e.g., scholarships. A balance should exist of motivational level to have an effective group dynamic. When one or two individuals lack the motivation to complete the assignment, friction and stress can easily develop, thus leading to a dysfunctional group. Students may become comfortable working with the same group once familiarity sets in, and that can impact level of motivation.

The disadvantages of working in groups can be overcome with a few strategies put into practice.

Form an inclusive environment

When first forming a group, take time to learn about the members in the group. Ask what courses they are taking, if they have a job, and what works best if assignments are required to be completed outside of class. Getting to know the members not only helps break the ice when meeting new people, but it also can initiate a conversation of how the group can best work together. Find if there are shared similar interests or if group members are taking the same courses to help form an environment of camaraderie. Making each other aware that everyone needs to play a role and that each member feels included in the group can ease and potentially alleviate feelings of isolation.

Assign roles

A discussion of what roles each member plays in the group will help with distributing responsibility. Groups can assign roles of a leader, writer, and reporter to create a group dynamic that is effective. The leader role can be responsible for ensuring that all members are participating and contributing to the assignment and that those assignments are turned in on time. The reporter role can assume responsibility for representing the team in class discussions. The writer role can jot down notes and questions for group and class discussion. Also, this role assumes responsibility that assignments are well-written.

Form a buddy system

Form a buddy system that will commit to calling each other to help overcome procrastination. This helps alleviate the pressure when deadlines are approaching. In interdisciplinary courses, motivation can vary greatly among students especially if the course is composed of students not only of different majors, but also from different colleges, e.g., science and business. A conversation about each student's priorities and how the class fits into those priorities allows students to be conscientious of their level of motivation for a particular course. Use the buddy system effectively to arrange calling each other at an agreed-upon time that each member committed to be working on the assignment. This will help each member to avoid procrastination.

Group Reassignment

Reassigning groups throughout the semester can recharge the student and reset the comfort level to help the student maintain a level of performance and stimulate energy. Students enrolled in Sci1301 (Research Foundations Course) were asked to voluntarily fill out a survey and answer questions about their preference for working in groups. The students overall favored group-change assignments throughout the semester (Figure 9.1). Interestingly, students also reported that working in groups helped their grades (Figure 9.2). Focusing on grades tends to be very stressful for most students, and in situations where the group experience becomes dysfunctional, that may negatively impact performance. Hence, a new group arrangement can accommodate some flexibility, and students can be assured that they will have an opportunity to experience a new group dynamic. The reassigning of groups gives students the opportunity for a fresh start and a chance to apply strategies that may not have been tried previously to form an effective group dynamic. What if the group dynamic is great and effective? Should reassignment take place? If a great group dynamic occurs within a group, the dynamic can be transferred to a new group and still continue to maintain camaraderie with the old group; it is a win-win situation.

Student's responses on a Likert Scale to questions of group work

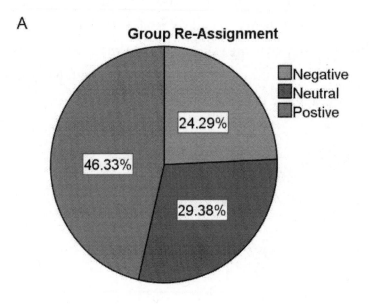

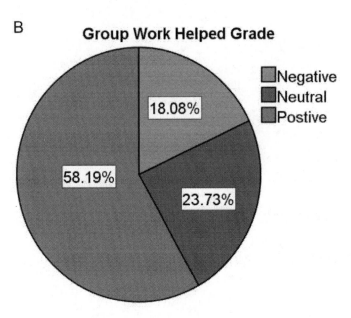

Figure 9.1

Group Personalities

There are personalities that affect the dynamic within a group. There are individuals that are highly motivated and have a "take-charge" approach to everything they do. Other individuals are more "laissez faire" with their approach and don't mind others taking the lead. Other individuals can be in the middle of the road; these individuals are more like "diplomats." The individuals that have a take-charge personality are often worried their grades may be compromised if the work is not done well. Therefore, that one individual may complete all the work by him- or herself. The laissez faire individual may stay back and allow others to make all the decisions. The diplomat assumes responsibility within the group but also is conscious of the fact that others also need to participate. Although the different personalities can determine the role each individual will play in the group, becoming aware of these personalities helps shape an effective group work dynamic. To form an effective team the members should strive a balance between the personalities.

Tackling Group Assignments

Effective group work does not happen by itself; it requires effort from both the instructor and students to work collaboratively. The instructor can facilitate the conditions to help group members work together effectively. An instructor may draft a group contract and mediate any issues that arise. The students follow the instructions set forth on the group contract and have discussions with group members when issues arise. A point system can be incorporated into group contracts that permit students to evaluate each other's group participation. Students must consider that each student has a full schedule and sometimes have jobs either on or off campus that have to be fit into the schedule. All members should have a calendar and mark the dates the assignments are due. Setting realistic deadlines to complete assignments can alleviate the pressure of completing multiple assignments. Marking the calendar together will help work around the different schedules. Usually the person that takes on the leader role assumes the responsibility of handing in the assignment. However, it is good practice that all members have a copy of the completed assignment in case the leader is unable to submit it on time. The phrase from Murphy's Law—"anything that can happen, will happen"—should always be assumed; hence, to ensure all assignments are completed and turned in on time, always have an alternative plan in case an unavoidable situation arises. The instructor should be promptly notified when unexpected circumstances arise.

Group Contract

The group contract helps the group teamwork effectively when all members are clear on what role they play in the group and what each member's responsibilities are to complete the assignments. Each member should try to put a full effort in completing the assignment. When one person fails to do his or her part, that responsibility falls on someone else and that can create tension within a group. Rather than talk behind a member's back, suggest a meeting to address the issue that may be causing more added stress. Use the group contract to help iron out issues (see Textbox Group Contract).

GROUP CONTRACT

Group work activity is part of the _____ course. Group contracts will be handed out at the beginning of the semester. Points awarded by the team members will make up _____% percent of the total grade (see grade breakdown).

Each group assignment has a team plan on the first page that required to be filled in. As specified in the team plan, group members will agree how the assignment must be completed amongst themselves. Also, each member must assume a role he or she will hold during that group assignment until completion. The three roles that a student can assume are leader, writer, or reporter.

The leader will be responsible for all members keeping with deadlines.

The writer's responsibility is to jot down any instructions or notes that will help the team complete the assignment. The writer can also jot down questions on behalf of the team.

The reporter will represent the team in class by asking questions and offering the group's perspective in class discussions.

Each different group assignment will require each team member to take a different role. Students cannot repeat the same role again until they have filled all three roles. Students can work on the same parts of the assignment and then combine efforts in group discussions.

Peer Evaluation Rubric

Members will award each other up to ___ points for each group assignment. The rubric can be downloaded with the group assignment. Once filled out, the rubric will be uploaded along with the group assignment. Each team member is responsible for uploading the assignment as well as his or her peer evaluation rubric for the other two group members.

As shown below, write the team member's name that will receive the points and the name of the person assigning the points. In the designated box, write the number of points awarded (0 to 5) for each category. The point average of two team members will be recorded on behalf of the third member.

If the team plan is not handed in with the group assignment or is incomplete, no points will be awarded toward the ___% group participation

Removing a Team Member

The group contract is an agreement among the group members that in the event two team members demonstrate that a member is not collaborating according to the specifications listed on the plan and the rubric, then the members can remove a member from the team. Reasons for removing a member can include missing agreed-upon deadlines if no notification was given to arrange for a new deadline, handing in incomplete work, missing class when in-class group assignments are issued; and not notifying team members when he or she is unable to join the group. If absent on a day when there is an in-class group assignment, only the members in attendance will receive points toward the group participation. With a valid absence excuse, the student can make up the group assignment; however, no group participation points will be awarded.

If a member is removed from the team, no points will be awarded toward the group assignment. The student will be placed in a new group. If removed from a second team throughout the semester, no further points will be awarded toward the ___% group participation. The group assignments are still required to be handed in. It is the group's responsibility to notify the instructor that a problem has developed among the group members and the issue must be addressed within the group with instructor mediation before the decision is made to remove a team member.

TEAM PLAN

What needs to be done?	Name of student who will do this part?	Must be completed by?

Writer	Leader	Reporter

PEER EVALUATION RUBRIC

Date					
Assignment					
Peer's Name					
Your Name					
Criteria	**0**	**1 or 2**	**3**	**4**	**5**
Attendance and contributing to assignments	Absent and no contribution on assignment	Absent but contributed minimally on outside-class assignment	Absent but contributed as agreed on outside-class assignment	Present and contributed less than agreed on in-class assignment	Present and contributed as agreed on in-class assignment
Tardiness	Absent or 30 minutes late	Late 21 to 29 minutes	Late 11 to 20 minutes	Late up to 10 minutes	Present at start of class time
Effort	Absent	No understanding of the material nor willingness to understand	Lacks some understanding and little willingness to understand	Demonstrates that understands the material	Demonstrates excellent understanding of the material and/ or willingness to explain to peers
Responsible and ethical conduct	Absent	Never courteous towards peers and / or instructor	Minimally courteous towards peers and / or instructor	Usually courteous towards peers and / or instructor	Consistently courteous towards peers and instructor
Total					

Disagreements

A professional demeanor should always be assumed in the classroom. What is a professional demeanor? Professional demeanor means being conscious of others' feelings and respecting boundaries. If a disagreement arises, refrain from insulting or gossiping about the peer. In the event that disagreements do occur, practice three key strategies: be realistic, be fair, and take the high road. Keep in mind that if issuing points to each other, those points are part of the overall grade. In keeping a realistic perspective, first be informed when members can hand in work because this may involve mainly the weekends or late at night. It is common for students who have afternoon jobs to work on their assignments late in the evening. If this is the case, arrange for an earlier deadline to ensure all of the components are completed on time. Be fair in assigning points when a peer member did not hold his or her end of the agreement but did do some work. Award points for the work that was completed rather than issuing zero points. Although emotions can run high when stressed, take the high road and attempt to talk it out with the group members before issuing points. It is best to voice any frustrations before issuing points and assigning zero points before having the chance to hear the other person's side of the story. Always seek the instructor's help to mediate any issues before the disagreement results in having to remove a member or the group becomes ineffective in completing assignments. Aiming for an effective group dynamic should be the focus working with the instructor and members of the group.

Refresher

Pursuing higher education can be an exciting time, providing the opportunity to achieve academic success. One of the first goals to put academic success into motion is having a balance between time allotted for classes and studying and time for personal matters. Managing schedules can make the difference in achieving milestones. To achieve milestones time should be invested in thinking about how to achieve the milestones or applying metacognition. Taking a proactive approach toward achieving academic success can be through active learning, which involves being aware and actively participating inside and outside the classroom to reach a higher understanding of the material. Active learning promotes grasping information that goes beyond memorization. In the classroom, the instructor can create opportunities to engage in active learning. The method of delivering material in the classroom can be designed to incorporate student participation to promote higher learning and refrain from lecture type of classrooms in which students mostly memorize material. Active learning can take place in an environment where material can be worked on with the collaboration of peers in groups. Forming groups in the classroom creates an environment that prompts action and motivates students to be engaged with the material and achieve learning. Working in groups to complete assignments can ease stress, share ideas, and develop camaraderie, which are all advantages of groups. However, when group members are not functioning at the same level of motivation, this can hinder the productivity of a group. The disadvantages of working in groups can be overcome by planning ahead and implementing strategies that will promote effective group work, such as having an inclusive environment and forming a buddy system. Also, reassignment to new groups throughout the semester can help students prevail over a bad experience and become recharged by meeting and working with new individuals. Different personalities can shape a group dynamic. The personalities that may be expressed are a "take-charge," a "laissez faire", or a "diplomatic" personality that can shape the dynamic of a group. Being aware which personality you most associate with helps work through issues to make an effective group dynamic. Group contracts can help establish ground rules that all group members abide by and can be reinforced through mediation from peers and the instructor. Disagreements cannot be avoided in all circumstances, though setting rules and displays of professional demeanor can help ease any tensions that may arise. The end goal of working in a group is to effectively learn the material and establish collaborative work.

End-of-Chapter Exercises: Applying Concepts

1. Name two strategies that can form an effective group.
2. As a group exercise, take 15 to 20 minutes to solve the word search puzzle (Figure 9.2), then answer the following questions:
    a. How did you work as a group to solve the task?
    b. What challenges did you experience during the exercise?
    c. What role ("take charge," "laissez faire," or "diplomatic") do you feel you primarily played in your group, and why?

What Is Science - Search Word Puzzle

```
Z  O  U  S  J  D  C  A  I  T  U  N  T  E  W
B  N  D  T  Y  X  R  N  C  J  F  B  0  Q  D
E  D  I  W  E  F  H  T  E  H  A  X  Z  U  U
D  T  U  A  R  N  O  U  V  U  R  J  V  G  B
G  H  P  P  K  A  O  I  V  I  M  D  S  U  I
T  E  F  I  N  S  B  I  Y  I  E  W  N  R  T
L  M  T  G  C  Y  E  B  N  T  E  W  N  R  T
M  P  V  R  Z  G  H  C  H  N  O  N  V  Q  R
W  I  E  U  M  A  I  L  X  B  X  R  Q  D  R
A  R  Y  F  Y  P  K  T  S  U  E  C  Y  Z  G
R  I  N  X  L  X  V  W  T  X  R  V  F  F  B
C  C  I  E  Y  N  H  C  Z  U  W  K  H  L  O
T  A  P  O  L  S  R  I  D  O  A  E  Y  Z  B
U  L  J  F  I  B  T  N  J  V  X  R  B  S  K
D  E  R  F  V  U  I  S  F  E  M  A  K  E  O
N  V  O  A  G  V  Z  C  Y  S  O  P  W  W  E
E  I  K  L  U  D  Q  O  U  J  T  R  C  F  A
X  D  R  S  K  D  C  L  Q  D  Z  V  N  S  L
Z  E  T  I  P  E  0  S  Y  O  O  H  F  K  I
A  N  W  F  H  U  I  E  M  T  J  R  I  A  U
H  C  U  I  W  L  M  Z  R  C  G  Q  P  N  Z
Y  E  Q  A  T  O  E  P  U  R  E  Y  E  U
F  E  G  B  X  T  V  B  V  A  B  V  H  X  R
K  S  C  I  I  J  H  Z  O  K  D  Z  U  P  B
Q  S  N  L  R  U  T  E  X  L  V  D  K  N  I
T  A  O  I  M  U  G  U  R  T  B  O  W  Q  H
D  D  E  T  B  R  F  S  G  E  P  I  Z  A  T
A  T  L  Y  S  D  P  A  O  I  T  M  I  P  Y
```

Hints: Write the terms that correspond with the hint

- Repeating   _____

- Observations   _____ _____

- Proving an hypothesis wrong _____ _____

                                     _____

Figure 9.2

Suggested Readings

Chapter 1: Who is the Novel Researcher?

- Bloomfield, V. A. & El-Fakahany, E. E. (2008). *The Chicago guide to your career in science: A toolkit for students and postdocs.* Chicago: The University of Chicago Press.

- Pain, E. (2015). Advice to a young scientist. *Science.* Retrieved from http://www.sciencemag.org/careers/2015/05/advice-young-scientist

Chapter 2: Defining Science

- Babkin, B.P. (1949). *Pavlov: A biography.* Chicago: University of Chicago Press.

- Fantoli, A. (2012). The case of Galileo: A closed question?. Notre Dame, IN.: University of Notre Dame Press.

- Godfrey-Smith. P. (2003). Popper: Conjecture and refutation. In *Theory and reality: An introduction to the philosophy of science* (pp. 57-74). Chicago: University of Chicago Press.

- Salmon, M.H., Earman. J., Glymour, C., Lennox, J.G.. Machamer, P., McGuire, J.E., ….(1999). Introductionto The Philosophy of Science, Indianapolis: Hackett Publishing Company, Inc.,

- Morange, M., (2008). What history tells us XIII. Fifty years of the Central Dogma J. Biosci. 33(2)pp. 171–175

- Nilsson, N. (2014). The scientific method. In *Understanding beliefs* (pp. 75-104). Cambridge, MA: MIT Press.

Chapter 3: Experimental Design

- Burns, R.B., (2000). Research Methods 4th ed. London: Sage Publications

- Taper, M.L., & Lele, S. R. (Eds). (2014). Experiments, observations, and other kinds of evidence. In *The nature of scientific evidence: Statistical, philosophical, and empirical considerations* (pp. 51-78). Chicago: University of Chicago Press.

- Vallery-Radot, R. (1886) Louis Pasteur: His life and labours. New York: D. Appleton and Company.

Chapter 4: Basic Statistics

- Popham, J. W. (1967). *Educational statistics: Use and interpretation.* New York: Harper & Row.
- Nevo, D. (2017). *Making sense of data through statistics: An introduction* (2nd ed). Legerity Digital Press.

Chapter 5: Scientific Literature

- Citation   formats http://subjectguides.library.american.edu/c.php?g=175008&p=1154150Bloomfield, V. A. & El-Fakahany, E. E. (2008). Writing a journal article. In *The Chicago guide to your career in science: A toolkit for students and postdocs* (pp. 323-334). Chicago: The University of Chicago Press.
- DeNeef, A. L. & Goodwin, C. D. (2006) Publishing in science. In *The academic's handbook* (pp. 306-314). Durham, NC: Duke University Press.
- Montgomery, S.L., (2003). The Chicago Guide to Communicating Science. Chicago: University of Chicago Press
-

Chapter 6: Ethics

- Bloomfield, V. A. & El-Fakahany, E. E. (2008). The meaning and responsible conduct of research. In *The Chicago guide to your career in science: A toolkit for students and postdocs* (pp. 151-169). Chicago: The University of Chicago Press.
- Institute of Medicine, National Academy of Engineering, & National Academy of Sciences. (2009). *On being a scientist: A guide to responsible conduct in research* (3rd ed). Washington, D.C.: The National Academies Press.

Chapter 7: Scientific Notebook

- Keeping a LabNotebookhttps://www.training.nih.gov/assets/Lab_Notebook_508_(new).pdf

Chapter 8: Communicating Science Through Presentations

- Alley, M. (2013). The craft of scientific presentations: Critical steps to succeed and critical errors to avoid, 2nd Ed. New York: Springer
- How to give a dynamic scientific presentation. https://www.elsevier.com/connect/how-to-give-a-dynamic-scientific-presentation
- Creating a 10-15 Minute Scientific Presentation. https://www.northwestern.edu/climb/resources/oral-communication-skills/creating-a-presentation.html

Chapter 9: Group Work

- Barkley, E.F., Cross, K.P., & Major, C.H. (2014). *Collaborative learning techniques: A handbook for college faculty* (2nd ed). Hoboken, NJ: Jossey-Bass.
- Beichner, R. (2007). The student-centered activities for large enrollment undergraduate programs (SCALE-UP) project. In *Research-based reform of University Physics* (1). Retrieved from https://www.compadre.org/Repository/document/ServeFile.cfm?ID=4517&DocID=183
- Freeman, S., Eddy, S. L., McDonough, M., Smith, M.K, Okoroafor, N., Jordt, H., & Wenderoth, M.P. (2014). Active learning increases student performance in science, engineering, and mathematics. *Proceedings of the National Academy of Sciences of the United States of America*, 111 (23), 8410-8415.
- Tsui, L. (2007). Effective strategies to increase diversity in STEM fields: A Review of the research literature. *The Journal of Negro Education,* 76 (4), 555-581.

Credit Lines

Table 6.1: Source: https://www.niehs.nih.gov/research/resources/bioethics/timeline/

Table 6.2: Source: https://history.nih.gov/about/timelines_laws_human.html#ant

Source: ELMER'S, "Elmer's Recipe for Colored Slime,"
http://www.elmers.com/projects/project/elmers-colored-recipe-slime.